10 ... tion ... especially to bring the reader a new awareness of the range, power and uses of the short-play form. The plays presented in the following pages have proven themselves to be among the most successful of their kind ever written.

M. JERRY WEISS, Chairman of the Department of Special Education and Reading, Jersey City State College, and the author of one of the plays in this collection, has served on various of the National Council of Teachers of English committees on the reading and teaching of drama. He is the author of several textbooks and guidance plays, and is the general editor of the Laurel-Leaf Library.

THE LAUREL-LEAF LIBRARY brings together under a single imprint outstanding works of fiction and nonfiction particularly suitable for young adult readers, both in and out of the classroom. This new series should also prove of great value to the general reader in search of knowledge, instruction and pleasure.

10 SHORT PLAYS

edited and introduced by M. JERRY WEISS

Published by DELL PUBLISHING CO., INC.
750 Third Avenue, New York 17, N.Y.

© *Copyright 1963, by M. Jerry Weiss*

DEDICATION: *To Helen, Lee, Harry and
Dorothy, Jeanette and David*

ACKNOWLEDGMENT: *For the biographical notes
on the authors of the plays in this collection
I am indebted to Melvin Cebulash*

First printing—October, 1963

Printed in U.S.A.

CONTENTS

INTRODUCTION

I am an avid playgoer and play-reader, and perhaps my best reason for editing this book is a hope of sharing my enthusiasm for the theater with others. To do this I have searched through dozens of plays to find the ones that I think best show the power and purposes of the short play.

Each play has a theme or central idea which the playwright hopes to get across through dialogue and action. A few characters are used to create a single impression growing out of the theme. It is not my intent to point out the central theme of each of the plays in this volume, for that would, indeed, spoil the pleasures of reading, discussing, and thinking about the plays and the effectiveness of the playwright. However, a variety of types is represented here. These include comedy, satire, poignant drama, historical and regional drama. To show the versatility of the short play, I have included a guidance play, a radio play and a television play.

Among the authors of the plays in this collection, Paul Green, Susan Glaspell, Maxwell Anderson, Thornton Wilder, William Saroyan, and Tennessee Williams have all received Pulitzer Prizes for their contributions to the theater. More information about the authors will be found at the end of this book.

To get the most out of reading these plays, try to picture the play on stage, with you, the reader, in the audience. The houselights dim. The curtains are about to open, and in a few minutes the action and dialogue will tell you the story.

M. JERRY WEISS

COMING THROUGH THE RYE

By William Saroyan

From Razzle-Dazzle, *copyright 1942 by William Saroyan. Reprinted by permission of Harcourt, Brace & World, Inc.*

A large room, beyond which is visible, in varying degrees of light and movement, infinite space. Sun, moon, planets, stars, constellations, and so on.

The room is one of many. It is The American Room, and is so marked.

Each person here has been conceived and is waiting to be born. Each possesses his ultimate physical form and ego. Ultimate, that is, in the sense that here, in this waiting room, he is the way he shall be the day he begins to die, or the day he dies, in the world.

The faces of the unconceived appear to be a white cloud of a summer afternoon.

A solemn but witty VOICE *speaks.*

THE VOICE

O.K., people. Your time has come. You are now going to enter the world. You'll find it a strange place. There are no instructions. You know your destiny now, but the moment you are in the world, breathing, you shall forget it. You can thank God for that, let me tell you. Good things, and bad, are ahead for each of you. The world is still new, and the idea of sending you out there for a visit has not yet proved itself to be a good one. It may in time, though. Your destination is America. [*A phrase of patriotic music.*] It's an interesting place. No better and no worse than any other place, except of course superficially, which the Americans make a good deal of, one way or the other. The climate's fair everywhere, excellent here and there. Everything you do, you shall imagine is your own doing. You can thank God for that, too. You shall live as long as you shall. No more. You will find noise and confusion everywhere, even in your sleep. Sometimes in sleep, however, you shall almost, but not quite, return to this place. Nothing in the world is important. Nothing is unimportant. Many things shall *seem* important. Many shall seem *unimportant*. In a moment you shall begin to be human. You have waited here nine months of the world's time. A few of you a little less. From now on you shall be alone in body, apparently cut off from everything. You shall also *seem* to be alone in spirit. That, however, is an illusion. Each of you is the continuation of two others, each of whom was a continuation of two others, each of whom— and so on. [*Blithely.*] I could go on talking for two or three years, but it wouldn't mean anything. O.K., now, here you go! Take a deep breath! [*Dramatically.*] Hold it! You will exhale in the world. O.K., Joe, let 'em out!

[*A few chords of music. Some* PEOPLE *go out.* BUTCH, *a boy of nine, and* MR. CARROLL, *a man of seventy, come in.* BUTCH *is thoughtfully bouncing an old tennis ball.*]

BUTCH

Well, we're next, Mr. Carroll. Do you like the idea of being born?

CARROLL

Why, yes, of course, Butch. There's nothing like getting born and being alive.

BUTCH

I don't know whether I'm lucky or unlucky. Steve says I'm lucky because I don't have to stay in the world very long, and Miss Quickly—she says it ain't fair.

CARROLL

What *ain't?*

BUTCH

Me having to get born, just for nine years. Before I get a chance to turn around I'll have to come back, so what's the use going? I'm the way I'm going to be when I die, and you're the way you're going to be when you die. I'm nine, and you're an old man.

CARROLL

Butch, my boy, those nine years are going to be wonderful.

BUTCH

Maybe. Miss Quickly says it'll take me five or six years just to begin. Gosh, that only leaves three. I won't even get a chance to see any big league baseball games.

CARROLL

Maybe you will.

BUTCH

Heck no. How am I going to get from a little town in Texas to New York?

CARROLL

It may happen.

BUTCH

Boy, I *hope* it does, but Miss Quickly—she told Steve it wasn't fair.

CARROLL

What wasn't?

BUTCH

My father dying before I'm born and my mother being poor, and dying a year later. She says I may have to go to an institution. What the heck's an institution?

CARROLL

That's an orphanage, I guess. Now, listen, Butch, don't

you go worrying about anything. Everything's wonderful out there.

BUTCH
How's it really going to be?

CARROLL
Well, the minute you're out there you're alive, the same as here, only different. Out there you begin right away.

BUTCH
Begin what?

CARROLL
Living—and dying. They're both beautiful, Butch. [*Happily.*] Living and dying in the world. That great big little tiny place. And from the first breath you take you begin being somebody: *yourself.*

BUTCH
I'm myself right now.

CARROLL
That's because you're here waiting. You've started at last. It takes a long time to get started. It took me—well, I don't know how long exactly in the world's time—but it was a long time.

BUTCH
Steve says the world stinks.

CARROLL
Now, Steve is a young fellow with ideas. He's a nice boy, but he's wrong about the world. It's the only place for us, and any of us who get to go out there are mighty lucky.

BUTCH
What happens when we leave the world?

CARROLL
We come back.

BUTCH

Here? And wait some more?

CARROLL

Not *here,* exactly. We wait *here, after* we've started. When we leave the world we go back to where we were before we came here.

BUTCH

Where the heck's that?

CARROLL

It's not exactly *any* place, Butch. And it's not exactly waiting either. *This* is where we *wait.*

BUTCH

Oh, well, I guess it'll be all right. But nine years. What the heck chance will I have to see anything?

CARROLL

Butch, one day out there is a long time, let alone nine years. Twenty-four hours every day. Sixty minutes every hour.

BUTCH

What are you going to be out there, Mr. Carroll?

CARROLL

[*Laughing.*] Oh, a lot of things, one after another.

BUTCH

Well, *what?*

CARROLL

Well, let's see. [*He brings out a paper and studies it.*] It says here, Thomas Carroll. Mother: Amy Wallace Carroll. Father: Jonathan Carroll. Will be, at birth: Son, brother, nephew, cousin, grandson, and so on.

BUTCH

Brother?

CARROLL

Yes. I guess I've got a sister or a brother out there, maybe a couple of sisters and a couple of brothers.

BUTCH

I thought we were all brothers. I thought everybody was related to everybody else.

CARROLL

Oh, yes, of course, but this kind of brotherhood is closer. Whoever my brother is, he has my father and mother for *his* father and mother.

BUTCH

Well, what the heck's the difference? I thought we were all the same.

CARROLL

Oh, we are, really, but in the world there are families. They're still all really one family, but in the world the family is broken down to the people you come from, and the people that come from you. It gets pretty complicated.

BUTCH

But everybody *is* one family just the same, though, ain't they?

CARROLL

Well, yes, but in the world everybody forgets that for a while.

BUTCH

[*Bringing out his paper, which is a good deal smaller than* CARROLL's.] What the heck. I never looked at this. What do I get to be? [*Reading the card.*] James Nelson, also called Butch. By gosh, there it is right there. Also called Butch, but my real name is James Nelson. Let's see what I get to be. [*Reading.*] Son. Newsboy. Schoolboy. [*Reflectively.*] Son. No brothers?

CARROLL
Well, I guess not, Butch.

BUTCH
Why the heck not?

CARROLL
There will be all sorts of kids out there in Texas. They'll
all be your brothers.

BUTCH
Honest?

CARROLL
Sure.

BUTCH
[*Reading.*] Newsboy. What's that?

CARROLL
Well, I guess you'll sell papers.

BUTCH
Is that good?

CARROLL
Now don't you worry about anything, Butch.

BUTCH
O.K. The heck with it. [*He puts the paper away.*]

CARROLL
[*Affectionately.*] Give me a catch, Butch.

BUTCH
[*Delighted.*] No fooling?

CARROLL
Why, sure, I'm going to play second base for the New
Haven Orioles.

BUTCH

[*Throwing the ball, which* CARROLL *tries to catch.*] Who the heck are they?

CARROLL

A bunch of kids in my neighborhood. [*He throws the ball back.*]

[STEVE *comes in. About twenty-seven, sober, serious, but a drunkard.* BUTCH *holds the ball and watches* STEVE. *Then goes to him.*]

BUTCH

Steve? Tell him about the war—and all that stuff.

STEVE

[*Scarcely noticing* BUTCH, *absorbed in thought.*] Tell *who, what?*

BUTCH

Mr. Carroll. About the war.

STEVE

[*Looking at* CARROLL, *smiling.*] I was talking to the old lady—

BUTCH

He means Miss Quickly.

STEVE

Yeah.

BUTCH

[*To* CARROLL.] If everybody is everybody else's brother, what the heck do they have a war for?

CARROLL

Well, now, Butch—

STEVE

[*Laughing solemnly.*] I'm afraid you won't be able to find

a good answer for that question, Doc.

BUTCH

[*Delighted.*] Honest, Steve?

CARROLL

Now, Steve, you know the world is a wonderful place.

STEVE

[*Simply.*] I'm sorry, but I think it stinks. I think the human race is unholy and disgusting. I think putting people in the world is a dirty trick.

CARROLL

No. No. No, it isn't, Steve.

STEVE

What is it, then? You're called out, everybody's a stranger, you suffer every kind of pain there is, and then you crawl back. A little tiny place that got side-tracked in space and began to fill up with terrible unclean animals in clothes.

CARROLL

Those *animals* have created several magnificent civilizations, and right now they're creating another one. It's a privilege to participate.

BUTCH

[*Delighted.*] You mean the World Series?

STEVE

[*Wearily.*] O.K., Doc. Anything you say.

CARROLL

Excuse me, Steve. Can I ask you a question?

STEVE

Anything at all.

CARROLL

What's ahead for you?

STEVE
A number of things.

CARROLL
Won't you tell me what they are?

STEVE
[*To* BUTCH.] How about it, kid? Come back in a few minutes.

BUTCH
Ah, shucks. I want to listen. I'm not born yet.

STEVE
This is nothing. I'll be seeing you.

BUTCH
[*Obedient, going to one side.*] O.K., Steve.

CARROLL
What is your destiny, Steve?

STEVE
[*Pause.*] Murder.

CARROLL
[*Amazed.*] Murder?

STEVE
[*Slowly.*] Yes. *I am going to murder* another human being.

CARROLL
Oh, I'm sorry, Steve.

STEVE
He's here, too.

CARROLL
Here? Who is he?

STEVE
I don't know if you've noticed him. *I* have. His name is

Hastings.

CARROLL

[*Shocked.*] Ralph Hastings?

STEVE

That's right.

CARROLL

Why, he's a nice young fellow. Are you sure it's not a mistake?

STEVE

No, it's not a mistake.

CARROLL

Well, good Lord. This is awful. But why? Why do you do it?

STEVE

It's a lot of nonsense.

CARROLL

What do you mean, Steve?

STEVE

You know he's rich. Well, he does a number of things that I think wreck the lives of poor people, so I—— If he's going to wreck the lives of people, what's he born for? If all I'm supposed to do is kill him, what am *I* born for?

CARROLL

I'm sorry, Steve. Of course you'll never know once you're out there.

STEVE

That'll help some, of course, but I just don't like the idea. What do *you* do, Doc?

CARROLL

Oh, nothing really.

STEVE
Do *you* kill anybody?

CARROLL
No, I don't, Steve. I do a lot of ordinary things.

STEVE
Do you raise a family?

CARROLL
[*Delighted, but shyly.*] Oh, yes. Three sons. Three daughters. All kinds of grandchildren.

STEVE
[*Sincerely.*] That's swell. That'll help a little.

CARROLL
Help? Help what?

STEVE
Help balance things.

CARROLL
Do *you* marry, Steve?

STEVE
Not exactly.

CARROLL
[*A little shocked but sympathetic.*] Oh?

STEVE
I get a lot of women, but not a *lot* of them. I get a year of one, though. That's toward the end. She's here. [*Smiling.*] I'm a little ashamed of myself.

CARROLL
Why should you be ashamed?

STEVE
Well, she's Peggy.

CARROLL
[*Shocked.*] Peggy?

STEVE
She'll probably be all right for me by that time.

CARROLL
Peggy's really a good girl, I suppose, but she seems so——

STEVE
I don't know her very well.

[MISS QUICKLY *enters, with* SEVEN KIDS, *ranging in age from three to thirteen:* ROOSEVELT, *colored, aged 3.* ALICE, *aged 5.* LARRY, *aged 7.* PEDRO GONZALEZ, *Mexican, aged 8.* JOHNNY GALLANTI, *Italian, aged 9.* BUTCH. HENRIETTA, *aged 13.*]

MISS QUICKLY
Now, children, what'll it be? Singing or play-acting?

SOME
Singing.

SOME
Play-acting.

ROOSEVELT
[*Emphatically, as if with a grudge.*] Nothing.

MISS QUICKLY
Nothing, Roosevelt? Now, really, you want to sing, don't you?

ROOSEVELT
No.

MISS QUICKLY
You want to act in a play, don't you?

ROOSEVELT
No.

MISS QUICKLY
You want to——

ROOSEVELT
No. I don't want to do nothing.

MISS QUICKLY
But *why,* Roosevelt?

ROOSEVELT
Because.

MISS QUICKLY
Because, what?

ROOSEVELT
Because I don't.

MISS QUICKLY
Don't you want to have fun?

ROOSEVELT
No.

MISS QUICKLY
[*Patiently.*] But why, child?

ROOSEVELT
Because.

MISS QUICKLY
Oh, dear.

STEVE
[*Calling.*] Come here, Roosevelt.

ROOSEVELT
[*Going to* STEVE.] She's always making us do stuff.

MISS QUICKLY
[*Gaily, to* STEVE.] Oh, thank you, Steve.
All right, children, we'll sing.

ROOSEVELT

[*Getting up into* STEVE'S *arms.*] They're going to sing! She's *always* making people sing, or something. [*Looking at* MISS QUICKLEY.] Shame on you!

STEVE

You stick with me, pardner.

ROOSEVELT

Wants 'em to play-act.

MISS QUICKLY

[*Sharply.*] All right, children! [*She blows the pitch.*] *Beautiful Dreamer* by Stephen Foster. Ready. One, two, three: Sing!

[MISS QUICKLY *and the* CHILDREN *sing the song.*]

That was fine, children. Now, Roosevelt, don't you want to sing?

ROOSEVELT

[*Opening his eyes.*] Shame on you—talk to me that way!

MISS QUICKLY

My gracious! Come along, children!

[*They go to one side.* RALPH HASTINGS *comes in, looks around. He is a well-dressed, decent sort of fellow, same age as* STEVE, *but younger looking. He looks at the colored boy, runs his hand through the kid's hair.*]

HASTINGS

How's the boy?

ROOSEVELT

No.

HASTINGS

[*Laughing.*] No, what?

ROOSEVELT
No, everything.

STEVE
[*Comforting him.*] O.K., kid.

ROOSEVELT
[*With anger.*] Only Steve's *my* pardner.

HASTINGS
Sure.

ROOSEVELT
Steve's the best man everywhere.

HASTINGS
[*Smiling at* STEVE.] Sure, he is.

CARROLL
[*Studying the two young men sadly.*] Well, Mr. Hastings, here we are.

HASTINGS
By the grace of God, here we wait for the first mortal breath. Are you pleased, Mr. Carroll?

CARROLL
I can't wait to begin.

HASTINGS
You, Steve?

STEVE
[*Simply.*] I'm here.

HASTINGS
And so am I. [*Pause.*] Well——

STEVE
Look. I don't know if you know, but if you do——

HASTINGS
As a matter of fact, I *do* know, but what the hell——!

STEVE
I want you to know——

HASTINGS
[*Cheerfully.*] It's all right.

CARROLL
[*Thoughtfully.*] There must be some mistake.

HASTINGS
No, there's no mistake. Everything's in order. I'm sorry, Steve. I'll have it coming to me, I suppose.

STEVE
I don't think so.

HASTINGS
These things all balance. I *must* have it coming to me.

STEVE
That's why I say the world stinks.

HASTINGS
It depends, I guess.

STEVE
[*Sincerely.*] Thanks. [*To* CARROLL.] Right now he's the way he is the day he dies, and I'm the way I am that day. It's obvious it's not him, and not me, so it *must* be the world.

HASTINGS
We're not human yet.

STEVE
You mean we're not inhuman yet.

CARROLL

Now, boys.

HASTINGS

[*Cheerfully.*] Of course, Mr. Carroll. [*To* STEVE.] I have a lot of fun, after a fashion, as long as it lasts. How about you?

STEVE

[*Laughs, stops.*] It's O.K.

[PEGGY *comes in, looks around, comes over to the three men. She simply stands near them.*]

You know—I like you, Peggy. Even here, you're lost.

PEGGY

Oh, it's boring—that's what burns me up. Nothing to do. No excitement. I want to get started, so I can get it over with. I want to dance—— I just heard a new one—— [*Singing.*] "I don't want to set the world on fire."

[CARROLL *and* HASTINGS *move away.*]

STEVE

Ah, now, Peggy—sure you do.

PEGGY

All I want to do is get it over with. I'm in a hurry. When do we start?

STEVE

[*He puts* ROOSEVELT *with the other kids.*] Any time, now— any minute. They just got rid of another mob. We're next. [*Pause, while he smiles at her.*] Near you, Peggy, I'm in a hurry myself. [*He takes her by the shoulders.*]

PEGGY

[*Shocked a little.*] Here?

STEVE

What's the difference? I've waited a long time for you.
[*He takes her and kisses her.*] You see, Peggy, you're no
good, and I love you for it. Because I'm no good, too. I
don't know why, but it's so. Now, before we know it, we'll
be separated and I won't be seeing you again for a long
time. Remember me, so that when we *do* meet again,
you'll know who I am.

PEGGY

I've got a poor memory, but I guess I'll know you just the
same.

STEVE

[*Kissing her again.*] You'll remember, don't worry.

[*They stand, kissing.*]

THE VOICE

O.K., people! Here we go again! I'm not going to go
through the whole speech. You're going out whether you
like it or not, so get going, and good luck to you!

[*Everybody goes. Only* STEVE *and* PEGGY *stand together,
kissing.*]

O.K., you two—get going!

[PEGGY *tries to move, but* STEVE *won't let her go.*]

Come on, come on, you American lovers, get going!

[PEGGY *struggles.* STEVE *holds her. She falls. He holds
her terribly.*]

PEGGY

[*Whispering.*] Let me go—please let me go!

[*They struggle passionately for some time.*]

THE VOICE

What's *this?* What goes on around here?

[*A whistle is blown, like a police whistle, but* STEVE *clings to* PEGGY. *At last* PEGGY *breaks away from him, gets to her feet, turns and runs.* STEVE *gets up and looks around, smiling wisely. He straightens out. As he stands, a new-born babe begins to bawl, as if it were himself being born. He looks around, turns easily, and walks out.*]

STEVE

O.K. O.K. I'm going.

THE CASE
OF THE
CRUSHED
PETUNIAS

A Lyrical Fantasy

By *Tennessee Williams*

This play is respectfully dedicated to the talent and charm of Miss Helen Hayes—Key West, February, 1941.

Copyright © 1948 by Tennessee Williams. Reprinted by permission of Ashley-Steiner, Inc.

CAST

Dorothy Simple
Police Officer
Young Man
Mrs. Dull

SCENE: *The action of the play takes place in the Simple Notion Shop, owned and operated by* MISS DOROTHY SIMPLE, *a New England maiden of twenty-six, who is physically very attractive but has barricaded her house and her heart behind a double row of petunias.*

The town is Primanproper, Massachusetts, which lies within the cultural orbit of Boston.

The play starts in the early morning. MISS SIMPLE, *very agitated for some reason, has just opened her little shop. She stands in the open door in a flood of spring sunlight, but her face expresses grief and indignation. She is calling to a* POLICE OFFICER *on the corner.*

DOROTHY
Officer?——Officer!

OFFICER
[*Strolling up to her.*] Yes, Miss Simple?

DOROTHY
I wish to report a case of deliberate and malicious sabotage!

OFFICER
Sabotage of what, Miss Simple?

DOROTHY
Of my petunias!

OFFICER
Well, well, well. Now what do you mean by that?

DOROTHY

Exactly what I said. You can see for yourself. Last night this house was surrounded by a beautiful double row of pink and lavender petunias. Look at them now! When I got up this morning I discovered them in this condition. Every single little petunia deliberately and maliciously crushed underfoot!

OFFICER

My goodness! Well, well, well!

DOROTHY

"Well, well, well" is not going to catch the culprit!

OFFICER

What do you want me to do, Miss Simple?

DOROTHY

I want you to apprehend a petuniacidal maniac with a size eleven D foot.

OFFICER

Eleven D?

DOROTHY

Yes. That is the size of the footprints that crushed my petunias. I just now had them measured by a shoe clerk.

OFFICER

That's a pretty large foot, Miss Simple, but lots of men have got large feet.

DOROTHY

Not in Primanproper, Massachusetts. Mr. Knowzit, the shoe clerk, assured me that there isn't a man in town who wears a shoe that size. Of course you realize the danger of allowing this maniac to remain at large. Any man who would crush a sweet petunia is equally capable in my opinion of striking a helpless woman or kicking an innocent child!

OFFICER

I'll do my best, Miss Simple. See yuh later.

DOROTHY

[*Curtly.*] Yes. Good-by. [*Slams door. She returns behind her notion counter and drums restively with her pale pink-polished nails. The canary cheeps timidly. Then tries an arpeggio.* DOROTHY, *to canary.*] Oh, hush up! [*Then contritely.*] Excuse me, please. My nerves are all to pieces!

[*Blows her nose. The doorbell tinkles as a customer enters. He is a* YOUNG MAN, *shockingly large and aggressive looking in the flower-papered cubicle of the shop.*]

Gracious, please be careful. You're bumping your head against my chandelier.

YOUNG MAN

[*Good-humoredly.*] Sorry, Miss Simple. I guess I'd better sit down. [*The delicate little chair collapses beneath him.*]

DOROTHY

Heaven have mercy upon us! You seem to have a genius for destruction! You've broken that little antique chair to smithereens!

YOUNG MAN

Sorry, Miss Simple.

DOROTHY

I appreciate your sorrow, but that won't mend my chair. —Is there anything I can show you in the way of notions?

YOUNG MAN

I'd like to see that pair of wine-colored socks you have in the window.

DOROTHY

What size socks do you wear?

YOUNG MAN

I keep forgetting. But my shoes are eleven D.

DOROTHY

[*Sharply.*] What size did you say? Eleven? Eleven D?

YOUNG MAN

That's right, Miss Simple. Eleven D.

DOROTHY

Oh. Your shoes are rather muddy, aren't they?

YOUNG MAN

That's right, Miss Simple, I believe they are.

DOROTHY

Quite muddy. It looks like you might have stepped in a freshly watered flower-bed last night.

YOUNG MAN

Come to think of it, that's what I did.

DOROTHY

I don't suppose you've heard about that horrible case of petunia crushing which occurred last night?

YOUNG MAN

As a matter of fact, I have heard something about it.

DOROTHY

From the policeman on the corner?

YOUNG MAN

No, ma'am. Not from him.

DOROTHY

Who from, then? He's the only man who knows about it except—except—except—the man who *did* it! [*Pause.*

The canary cheeps inquiringly.] You—you—*you*—are the man who *did* it!

YOUNG MAN
Yes, Miss Simple. I am the man who did it.

DOROTHY
Don't try to get away!

YOUNG MAN
I won't, Miss Simple.

DOROTHY
Stand right where you are till the officer comes!

YOUNG MAN
You're going to call the officer?

DOROTHY
Yes, I am, I certainly am.—In a minute. First I'd like to ask you *why* you *did* it? Why did you crush my petunias?

YOUNG MAN
Okay. I'll tell you why. First, because you'd barricaded your house—and also your heart—behind that silly little double row of petunias!

DOROTHY
Barricaded? My house—my heart—behind them? That's absurd. I don't know what you mean.

YOUNG MAN
I know. They're apparently such delicate, fragile creatures, these petunias, but they have a terrible resistance.

DOROTHY
Resistance to what, may I ask?

YOUNG MAN
Anything big or important that happens to come by your house. Nothing big or important can ever get by a double

row of petunias! That is the reason why you are living alone with your canary and beginning to dislike it.

DOROTHY
Dislike my canary? I love it!

YOUNG MAN
Secretly, Miss Simple, you wish the bird-seed would choke it! You dislike it nearly as much as you secretly disliked your petunias.

DOROTHY
Why should I, why should you, why should anybody dislike petunias!

YOUNG MAN
Our animosity and its resultant action is best explained by a poem I once composed on the subject of petunias— and similar flora. Would you like to hear it?

DOROTHY
I suppose I should, if it's relevant to the case.

YOUNG MAN
Extremely relevant. It goes like this:

[LIGHT MUSIC:]
How grimly do petunias look
on things not listed in the book,
For these dear creatures never move
outside the academic groove.
They mark with sharp and moral eye
phenomena that pass them by
And classify as good or evil
mammoth whale or tiny weevil.
They note with consummate disdain
all that is masculine or plain.
They blush down to their tender roots
when men pass by in working boots.

All honest language shocks them so
they cringe to hear a rooster crow.
Of course they say that good clean fun's
permissible for *every* one
But find that even Blindman's Bluff
is noisy and extremely rough
AND—[*Stage whisper.*]
—Not quite innocent enough!

What do you think of it?

DOROTHY
Unfair! Completely unfair!

YOUNG MAN
[*Laughing.*] To organized petunias?

DOROTHY
Yes, and besides, I don't think anyone has the right to impose his opinions in the form of footprints on other people's petunias!

YOUNG MAN
[*Removing small package from pocket.*] I'm prepared to make complete restitution.

DOROTHY
What with?

YOUNG MAN
With these.

DOROTHY
What are they?

YOUNG MAN
Seeds.

DOROTHY
Seeds of what? Sedition?

YOUNG MAN
No. Wild roses.

DOROTHY
Wild? I couldn't use them!

YOUNG MAN
Why not, Miss Simple?

DOROTHY
Flowers are like human beings. They can't be allowed to grow wild. They have to be——

YOUNG MAN
Regimented? Ahhh. I see. You're a horticultural fascist!

DOROTHY
[*With an indignant gasp.*] I ought to call the policeman about those petunias!

YOUNG MAN
Why don't you, then?

DOROTHY
Only because you made an honest confession.

YOUNG MAN
That's not why, Miss Simple.

DOROTHY
No?

YOUNG MAN
The actual reason is that you are fascinated.

DOROTHY
Am I? Indeed!

YOUNG MAN
Indeed you are, Miss Simple. In spite of your late un-lamented petunias, you're charmed, you're intrigued——

you're frightened!

DOROTHY
You're very conceited!

YOUNG MAN
Now, if you please, I'd like to ask you a question.

DOROTHY
You may. But I may not answer.

YOUNG MAN
You will if you can. But you probably won't be able. The question is this: What do you make of it all?

DOROTHY
I don't understand—— All *what?*

YOUNG MAN
The world? The universe? And your position in it? This miraculous accident of being alive! [*Soft music background.*] Has it ever occurred to you how much the living are outnumbered by the dead? Their numerical superiority, Miss Simple, is so tremendous that you couldn't possibly find a ratio with figures vast enough *above* the line, and small enough *below* to represent it.

DOROTHY
You sound like you were trying to sell me something.

YOUNG MAN
I am, I am, just wait!

DOROTHY
I'm not in the market for——

YOUNG MAN
Please! One minute of your infinitely valuable time!

DOROTHY
All right. One minute.

YOUNG MAN
Look!

DOROTHY
At what?

YOUNG MAN
Those little particles of dust in the shaft of April sunlight through that window.

DOROTHY
What about them?

YOUNG MAN
Just think. You might have been one of those instead of what you are. You might have been any one of those infinitesimal particles of dust. Or any one of millions and billions and trillions of other particles of mute, unconscious matter. Never capable of asking any questions. Never capable of giving any answers. Never capable of doing, thinking, feeling anything at all! But instead, dear lady, by the rarest and most improbable of accidents, you happened to be what you are. Miss Dorothy Simple from Boston! Beautiful. Human. Alive. Capable of thought and feeling and action. Now here comes the vital part of my question. What are you going to *do* about it, Miss Simple?

DOROTHY
[*Who is somewhat moved, in spite of her crushed petunias.*] Well, goodness—gracious—sakes alive! I thought you came in here to buy some socks?

YOUNG MAN
Yes, but I've got to sell *you* something first.

DOROTHY
Sell me what?

YOUNG MAN
A wonderful bill of goods.

DOROTHY
I'll have to see it before I sign the order.

YOUNG MAN
That's impossible. I can't display my samples in this shoppe.

DOROTHY
Why not?

YOUNG MAN
They're much too precious. You have to make an appointment.

DOROTHY
[*Retreating.*] Sorry. But I do all my business in here.

YOUNG MAN
Too bad for you.—In fact, too bad for us both. Maybe you'll change your mind?

DOROTHY
I don't think so.

YOUNG MAN
Anyway, here's my card.

DOROTHY
[*Reading it, bewildered.*]—LIFE—INCORPORATED. [*Looks up slowly.*]

YOUNG MAN
Yes. I represent that line.

DOROTHY
I see. You're a magazine salesman?

YOUNG MAN
No. It isn't printed matter.

DOROTHY
But it's matter, though?

YOUNG MAN

Oh, yes, and it's matter of tremendous importance, too. But it's neglected by people. Because of their ignorance they've been buying cheap substitute products. And lately a rival concern has sprung up outside the country. This firm is known as "Death, Unlimited." Their product comes in a package labeled "War." They're crowding us out with new aggressive methods of promotion. And one of their biggest sales points is "Excitement." Why does it work so well? Because you little people surround your houses and also your hearts with rows of tiresome, trivial little things like petunias! If we could substitute wild roses, there wouldn't be wars! No, there'd be excitement enough in the world *without* having wars! That's why we've started this petunia-crushing campaign, Miss Simple. "Life, Incorporated" has come to the realization that we have to use the same aggressive methods of promotion used by "Death, Unlimited," over there! We've got to show people that the malignantly trivial little petunias of the world can be eliminated more cleanly, permanently and completely by "Life, Incorporated" than by "Death, Unlimited!" Now what do you say, Miss Simple? Won't you try our product?

DOROTHY

[*Nervously.*] Well, you see it's like this—I do all my buying in Boston and——

YOUNG MAN

What do you buy in Boston?

DOROTHY

You can see for yourself. Look over the stock.

YOUNG MAN

[*Examining the shelves.*] Thimbles—threads—ladies' needle-work—white gloves——

DOROTHY
Notions. Odds and ends.

YOUNG MAN
Odds and ends—of existence?

DOROTHY
Yes, that's it exactly.

YOUNG MAN
What do you do after hours?

DOROTHY
I carry on a lot of correspondence.

YOUNG MAN
Who with?

DOROTHY
With wholesale firms in Boston.

YOUNG MAN
How do you sign your letters?

DOROTHY
"Sincerely." "As ever." "Very truly yours."

YOUNG MAN
But never with love?

DOROTHY
Love? To firms in Boston?

YOUNG MAN
I guess not. I think you ought to enlarge your correspondence. I'll tell you what I'll do. I'll meet you tonight on Highway No. 77!

DOROTHY
Oh, no! I have my correspondence!

YOUNG MAN

Delay your correspondence. Meet me there. We'll have a couple of beers at the Starlight Casino.

DOROTHY

[*With frantic evasion.*] But I don't drink!

YOUNG MAN

Then *eat.* Swiss cheese on rye. It doesn't matter. Afterwards I'll take you for a ride in an open car.

DOROTHY

Where to?

YOUNG MAN

To Cypress Hill.

DOROTHY

Why, that's the cemetery.

YOUNG MAN

Yes, I know.

DOROTHY

Why there?

YOUNG MAN

Because dead people give the best advice.

DOROTHY

Advice on what?

YOUNG MAN

The problems of the living.

DOROTHY

What advice do they give?

YOUNG MAN

Just one word: *Live!*

DOROTHY
Live?

YOUNG MAN
Yes, live, live, live! It's all they know, it's the only word
left in their vocabulary!

DOROTHY
I don't see how——?

YOUNG MAN
I'll tell you how. There's one thing in Death's favor. It's a
wonderful process of simplification. It rids the heart of all
inconsequentials. For instance, it goes through the dic-
tionary with an absolutely merciless blue pencil. Finally
all that you've got left's one page—and on that page one
word!

DOROTHY
The word you hear at night on Cypress Hill?

YOUNG MAN
The word you hear at night on Cypress Hill!

DOROTHY
Ohhh. Oh, oh!

YOUNG MAN
But no one hears it till they deal with *me*. I have a secret
patented device that makes it audible to them. Something
never processed by Du Pont. But none the less a marvelous
invention. It's absolutely weightless and transparent. It
fits inside the ear. Your friends won't even know you have
it on. But this I guarantee: you'll hear that word, that
sound much like the long, sweet sound of leaves in motion!

DOROTHY
Leaves?

YOUNG MAN

Yes, willow leaves or leaves of cypresses or leaves of wind-blown grass! And afterwards you'll never be the same. No, you'll be changed forever!

DOROTHY

In what way?

YOUNG MAN

You'll live, live, *live!*—And not behind petunias. How about it, Miss Simple? Dorothy? Is it a date? Tonight at half-past eight on No. 77?

DOROTHY

Whereabouts on Highway No. 77?

YOUNG MAN

By the wild plum-tree—at the broken place in the long stone wall—where roots have cleft the rocks and made them crumble.

DOROTHY

It sounds so far. It sounds—uncivilized.

YOUNG MAN

It is uncivilized, but it isn't far.

DOROTHY

How would I get out there? What means of transportation?

YOUNG MAN

Borrow your kid brother's bike.

DOROTHY

Tonight's Scout meeting night; he wouldn't let me.

YOUNG MAN

Then walk, it wouldn't kill you!

DOROTHY
How do you know? It might. I come from Boston.

YOUNG MAN
Listen, lady. Boston's a state of mind that you'll grow out of.

DOROTHY
Not without some insulin shock treatments.

YOUNG MAN
Stop evading! Will you or will you not?

DOROTHY
I've got so much to do. I have to return some books to the public library.

YOUNG MAN
Just one more time—will you or will you not?

DOROTHY
I can't give definite answers—I'm from Boston!

YOUNG MAN
Just one more mention of Boston's apt to be fatal! Well, Miss Simple? I can't wait forever!

DOROTHY
I guess I—might.

YOUNG MAN
You guess you *might?*

DOROTHY
I mean I guess I will.

YOUNG MAN
You *guess* you will?

DOROTHY
I mean I will—I *will!*

YOUNG MAN

That's better.—So long, Dorothy. [*He grins and goes out, slamming door.*]

DOROTHY

Good-by. [*She stares dreamily into space for a moment.* MRS. DULL *comes in.*]

MRS. DULL

[*Sharply.*] Miss Simple!

DOROTHY

Oh! Excuse me. What do you want?

MRS. DULL

I want a pair of wine-colored socks for my husband.

DOROTHY

I'm terribly sorry but the only pair in stock have been reserved.

MRS. DULL

Reserved for whom, Miss Simple?

DOROTHY

A gentleman who represents this line. [*Showing card.*]

MRS. DULL

"Life, Incorporated"? Huh, I never heard of it.

DOROTHY

Neither had I before. But now I have. And tomorrow the store will be closed for extensive alterations.

MRS. DULL

Alterations of what kind, Miss Simple?

DOROTHY

I'm going to knock out all four walls.

MRS. DULL

Knock out—what——? Incredible!

DOROTHY

Yes, to accommodate some brand-new merchandise. Things I never kept in stock before.

MRS. DULL

What kind of things? Things in bottles, Miss Simple, or things in boxes?

DOROTHY

Neither one nor the other, Mrs. Dull.

MRS. DULL

But everything comes in bottles or in boxes.

DOROTHY

Everything but "Life, Incorporated."

MRS. DULL

What does it come in, then?

DOROTHY

I'm not sure yet. But I suspect it's something unconfined, something wild and open as the sky is!—Also I'm going to change the name of the store. It isn't going to be "Simple Notions" any more, it's going to be "Tremendous Inspirations!"

MRS. DULL

Gracious! In that case you'll certainly lose my custom.

DOROTHY

I rather expected to.

MRS. DULL

And you're not sorry?

DOROTHY

Not the least bit sorry. I think I caught a slight skin rash from dealing with your silver. Also you sniff too much. You ought to blow your nose. Or better still, you ought to trim it down. I've often wondered how you get your nose through traffic.

[MRS. DULL *gasps, looks desperately about her, rushes out.*]

You forgot your groceries, Mrs. Dull! [*Heaves them out the door.*]

[*Loud impact, sharp outcry. Music up.*]

Officer?—Officer!

OFFICER
Did you say size eleven D, Miss Simple?

DOROTHY
Never mind that now, that's all been settled.

OFFICER
Amicably? Out of court, you mean?

DOROTHY
Amicably and out of court. The saboteur has made full restitution and the case is dropped. Now what I want to ask of you is this: how do I get out to No. 77?

OFFICER
Highway No. 77? That road's abandoned.

DOROTHY
Not by me. Where is it?

OFFICER
It's in an awful condition, it's overgrown by brambles!

DOROTHY
I don't care! Where is it?

OFFICER
They say the rain has loosened half the stones. Also the wind has taken liberties with it. The moon at night makes

such confusing shadows people lose their way, go danger-
ous places, do outrageous things!

DOROTHY
Things such as what?

OFFICER
Oh—senseless acrobatics, cart-wheels in mid-air, unheard
of songs they sing, distil the midnight vapors into wine—
do pagan dances!

DOROTHY
Marvelous! How do I get there?

OFFICER
I warn you, Miss Simple, once you go that way you can't
come back to Primanproper, Massachusetts!

DOROTHY
Who wants to come back here? Not I! Never was anyone
a more willing candidate for expatriation than I am tonight! All I want to know is where it is— Is it north, south,
or east or west of town?

OFFICER
That's just it, ma'am. It's in all four directions.

DOROTHY
Then I don't suppose that I could possibly miss it.

OFFICER
Hardly possibly, if you want to find it. Is that all?

DOROTHY
Yes, sir, that's all.—Thanks very much.—Good-by! [*Music
up.* DOROTHY *softly.*] Good-by forever!

THE HAPPY JOURNEY TO TRENTON AND CAMDEN

By Thornton Wilder

CAST

The Stage Manager
Ma Kirby
Arthur Kirby
Caroline Kirby
Elmer Kirby (Pa)
Beulah

No scenery is required for this play. Perhaps a few dusty flats may be seen leaning against the brick wall at the back of the stage.

The five members of the Kirby family and THE STAGE MANAGER *compose the cast.* THE STAGE MANAGER *not only moves forward and withdraws the few properties that are required, but he reads from a typescript the lines of all the minor characters. He reads them clearly, but with little attempt at characterization, scarcely troubling himself to alter his voice, even when he responds in the person of a child or a woman.*

As the curtain rises THE STAGE MANAGER *is leaning lazily against the proscenium pillar at the audience's left. He is smoking.*

ARTHUR *is playing marbles in the center of the stage.*

CAROLINE *is at the remote back, right, talking to some girls who are invisible to us.*

MA KIRBY *is anxiously putting on her hat before an imaginary mirror.*

M A

Where's your pa? Why isn't he here? I declare we'll never get started.

ARTHUR

Ma, where's my hat? I guess I don't go if I can't find my hat.

M A

Go out into the hall and see if it isn't there. Where's Caroline gone to now, the plagued child?

ARTHUR

She's out waitin' in the street talkin' to the Jones girls.—
I just looked in the hall a thousand times, Ma, and it isn't
there. [*He spits for good luck before a difficult shot and
mutters.*] Come on, baby.

MA

Go and look again, I say. Look carefully.

[ARTHUR *rises, runs to the right, turns around swiftly,
returns to his game, flinging himself on the floor with a
terrible impact, and starts shooting an aggie.*]

ARTHUR

No. Ma, it's not there.

MA

[*Serenely.*] Well, you don't leave Newark without that
hat, make up your mind to that. I don't go no journeys
with a hoodlum.

ARTHUR

Aw, Ma!

[MA *comes down to the footlights and talks toward the
audience as through a window.*]

MA

Oh, Mrs. Schwartz!

THE STAGE MANAGER

[*Consulting his script.*] Here I am, Mrs. Kirby. Are you
going yet?

MA

I guess were going in just a minute. How's the baby?

THE STAGE MANAGER

She's all right now. We slapped her on the back and she
spat it up.

MA

Isn't that fine!—Well now, if you'll be good enough to give the cat a saucer of milk in the morning and the evening, Mrs. Schwartz, I'll be ever so grateful to you.—Oh, good afternoon Mrs. Hobmeyer!

THE STAGE MANAGER

Good afternoon, Mrs. Kirby, I hear you're going away.

MA

[*Modest.*] Oh, just for three days, Mrs. Hobmeyer, to see my married daughter Beulah, in Camden. Elmer's got his vacation week from the laundry early this year, and he's just the best driver in the world.

[CAROLINE *comes "into the house" and stands by her mother.*]

THE STAGE MANAGER

Is the whole family going?

MA

Yes, all four of us that's here. The change ought to be good for the children. My married daughter was downright sick a while ago——

THE STAGE MANAGER

Tchk—tchk—tchk! Yes. I remember you tellin' us.

MA

And I just want to go down and see the child. I ain't seen her since then. I just won't rest easy in my mind without I see her. [*To* CAROLINE.] Can't you say good afternoon to Mrs. Hobmeyer?

CAROLINE

[*Blushes and lowers her eyes and says woodenly.*] Good afternoon, Mrs. Hobmeyer.

THE STAGE MANAGER

Good afternoon, dear.—Well, I'll wait and beat these
rugs until after you're gone, because I don't want to choke
you. I hope you have a good time and find everything all
right.

MA

Thank you, Mrs. Hobmeyer, I hope I will.—Well, I guess
that milk for the cat is all, Mrs. Schwartz, if you're sure
you don't mind. If anything should come up, the key to
the back door is hanging by the icebox.

ARTHUR and CAROLINE

Ma! Not so loud. Everybody can hear yuh.

MA

Stop pullin' my dress, children. [*In a loud whisper.*] The
key to the back door I'll leave hangin' by the icebox and
I'll leave the screen door unhooked.

THE STAGE MANAGER

Now have a good trip, dear, and give my love to Loolie.

MA

I will, and thank you a thousand times. [*She returns "into
the room."*] What can be keeping your pa?

ARTHUR

I can't find my hat, Ma.

[*Enter* ELMER *holding a hat.*]

ELMER

Here's Arthur's hat. He musta left it in the car Sunday.

MA

That's a mercy. Now we can start.—Caroline Kirby, what
you done to your cheeks?

CAROLINE

[*Defiant, abashed.*] Nothin'.

MA

If you've put anything on 'em, I'll slap you.

CAROLINE

No, Ma, of course I haven't. [*Hanging her head.*] I just rubbed'm to make'm red. All the girls do that at high school when they're goin' places.

MA

Such silliness I never saw. Elmer, what kep' you?

ELMER

[*Always even-voiced and always looking out a little anxiously through his spectacles.*] I just went to the garage and had Charlie give a last look at it, Kate.

MA

I'm glad you did. I wouldn't like to have no breakdown miles from anywhere. Now we can start. Arthur, put those marbles away. Anybody'd think you didn't want to go on a journey to look at yuh.

[*They go out through the "hall," take the short steps that denote going downstairs, and find themselves in the street.*]

ELMER

Here, you boys, you keep away from that car.

MA

Those Sullivan boys put their heads into everything.

[THE STAGE MANAGER *has moved forward four chairs and a low platform. This is the automobile. It is in the center of the stage and faces the audience. The platform slightly raises the two chairs in the rear.* PA's *hands hold an imaginary steering wheel and continu-*

ally shift gears. CAROLINE *sits beside him.* ARTHUR *is behind him and* MA *behind* CAROLINE.]

CAROLINE
[*Self-consciously.*] Good-by, Mildred. Good-by, Helen.

THE STAGE MANAGER
Good-by, Caroline. Good-by, Mrs. Kirby. I hope y' have a good time.

MA
Good-by, girls.

THE STAGE MANAGER
Good-by, Kate. The car looks fine.

MA
[*Looking upward toward a window.*] Oh, good-by, Emma! [*Modestly.*] We think it's the best little Chevrolet in the world.—Oh, good-by, Mrs. Adler!

THE STAGE MANAGER
What, are you going away, Mrs. Kirby?

MA
Just for three days, Mrs. Adler, to see my married daughter in Camden.

THE STAGE MANAGER
Have a good time.

[*Now* MA, CAROLINE, *and* THE STAGE MANAGER *break out into a tremendous chorus of good-bys. The whole street is saying good-by.* ARTHUR *takes out his peashooter and lets fly happily into the air. There is a lurch or two and they are off.*]

ARTHUR
[*In sudden fright.*] Pa! Pa! Don't go by the school. Mr. Biedenbach might see us!

MA

I don't care if he does see us. I guess I can take my children out of school for one day without having to hide down back streets about it. [ELMER *nods to a passer-by.* MA *asks without sharpness.*] Who was that you spoke to, Elmer?

ELMER

That was the fellow who arranges our banquets down to the Lodge, Kate.

MA

Is he the one who had to buy four hundred steaks? [PA *nods.*] I declare, I'm glad I'm not him.

ELMER

The air's getting better already. Take deep breaths, children.

[*They inhale noisily.*]

ARTHUR

Gee, it's almost open fields already. "*Weber and Heilbronner Suits for Well-dressed Men.*" Ma, can I have one of them someday?

MA

If you graduate with good marks perhaps your father'll let you have one for graduation.

CAROLINE

[*Whining.*] Oh, Pa! Do we have to wait while that whole funeral goes by?

[PA *takes off his hat.* MA *cranes forward with absorbed curiosity.*]

MA

Take off your hat, Arthur. Look at your father.—Why, Elmer, I do believe that's a lodge brother of yours. See the banner? I suppose this is the Elizabeth branch.

[ELMER *nods.* MA *sighs: Tchk—tchk—tchk. They all lean forward and watch the funeral in silence, growing momentarily more solemnized. After a pause,* MA *continues almost dreamily.*]

Well, we haven't forgotten the one that went on, have we? We haven't forgotten our good Harold. He gave his life for his country, we mustn't forget that. [*She passes her finger from the corner of her eye across her cheek. There is another pause.*] Well, we'll all hold up the traffic for a few minutes someday.

THE CHILDREN
[*Very uncomfortable.*] Ma!

MA
[*Without self-pity.*] Well I'm "ready," children. I hope everybody in this car is "ready." [*She puts her hand on* PA'S *shoulder.*] And I pray to go first, Elmer. Yes. [PA *touches her hand.*]

THE CHILDREN
Ma, everybody's looking at you. Everybody's laughing at you.

MA
Oh, hold your tongues! I don't care what a lot of silly people in Elizabeth, New Jersey, think of me.—Now we can go on. That's the last. [*There is another lurch and the car goes on.*]

CAROLINE
"Fit-Rite Suspenders. The Working Man's Choice." Pa, why do they spell "Rite" that way?

ELMER
So that it'll make you stop and ask about it, missy.

CAROLINE

Papa, you're teasing me.—Ma, why do they say *"Three Hundred Rooms Three Hundred Baths"?*

ARTHUR

"Miller's Spaghetti: The Family's Favorite Dish." Ma, why don't you ever have spaghetti?

MA

Go along, you'd never eat it.

ARTHUR

Ma, I like it now.

CAROLINE

[*With a gesture.*] Yum-yum. It looks wonderful up there. Ma, make some when we get home?

MA

[*Dryly.*] "The management is always happy to receive suggestions. We aim to please."

[*The whole family finds this exquisitely funny. The children scream with laughter. Even* ELMER *smiles.* MA *remains modest.*]

ELMER

Well, I guess no one's complaining, Kate. Everybody knows you're a good cook.

MA

I don't know whether I'm a good cook or not, but I know I've had practice. At least I've cooked three meals a day for twenty-five years.

ARTHUR

Aw, Ma, you went out to eat once in a while.

MA

Yes. That made it a leap year.

[This joke is no less successful than its predecessor. When the laughing dies down, CAROLINE *turns around in an ecstasy of well-being and kneeling on the cushions, says.]*

CAROLINE

Ma, I love going out in the country like this. Let's do it often, Ma.

MA

Goodness, smell that air, will you! It's got the whole ocean in it.—Elmer, drive careful over that bridge. This must be New Brunswick we're coming to.

ARTHUR

[Jealous of his mother's successes.] Ma, when is the next comfort station?

MA

[Unruffled.] You don't want one. You just said that to be awful.

CAROLINE

[Shrilly.] Yes, he did, Ma. He's terrible. He says that kind of thing right out in school and I want to sink through the floor, Ma. He's terrible.

MA

Oh, don't get so excited about nothing, Miss Proper! I guess we're all yewman beings in this car, at least as far as I know. And Arthur, you try and be a gentleman.—Elmer, don't run over that collie dog. *[She follows the dog with her eyes.]* Looked kinda peakèd to me. Needs a good honest bowl of leavings. Pretty dog, too. *[Her eyes fall on a billboard.]* That's a pretty advertisement for Chesterfield cigarettes, isn't it? Looks like Beulah, a little.

ARTHUR
Ma?

MA

Yes.

ARTHUR

[*"Route" rhymes with "out."*] Can't I take a paper route with the *Newark Daily Post?*

MA

No, you cannot. No, sir. I hear they make the paper boys get up at four-thirty in the morning. No son of mine is going to get up at four-thirty every morning, not if it's to make a million dollars. Your *Saturday Evening Post* route on Thursday mornings is enough.

ARTHUR

Aw, Ma.

MA

No, sir. No son of mine is going to get up at four-thirty and miss the sleep God meant him to have.

ARTHUR

[*Sullenly.*] Hhm! Ma's always talking about God. I guess she got a letter from him this morning.

[MA *rises, outraged.*]

MA

Elmer, stop that automobile this minute. I don't go another step with anybody that says things like that. Arthur, you get out of this car. Elmer, you give him another dollar bill. He can go back to Newark by himself. I don't want him.

ARTHUR

What did I say? There wasn't anything terrible about that.

ELMER

I didn't hear what he said, Kate.

M A

God has done a lot of things for me and I won't have him made fun of by anybody. Go away. Go away from me.

C A R O L I N E

Aw, Ma—don't spoil the ride.

M A

No.

E L M E R

We might as well go on, Kate, since we've got started. I'll talk to the boy tonight.

M A

[*Slowly conceding.*] All right, if you say so, Elmer. But I won't sit beside him. Caroline, you come and sit by me.

A R T H U R

[*Frightened.*] Aw, Ma, that wasn't so terrible.

M A

I don't want to talk about it. I hope your father washes your mouth out with soap and water.—Where'd we all be if I started talking about God like that, I'd like to know! We'd be in the speakeasies and night clubs and places like that, that's where we'd be.—All right, Elmer, you can go on now.

C A R O L I N E

What did he say, Ma? I didn't hear what he said.

M A

I don't want to talk about it.

[*They drive on in silence for a moment, the shocked silence after a scandal.*]

E L M E R

I'm going to stop and give the car a little water, I guess.

MA

All right, Elmer. You know best.

ELMER

[*To a garage hand.*] Could I have a little water in the radiator—to make sure?

THE STAGE MANAGER

[*In this scene alone he lays aside his script and enters into a role seriously.*] You sure can. [*He punches the tires.*] Air all right? Do you need any oil or gas?

ELMER

No, I think not. I just got fixed up in Newark.

MA

We're on the right road for Camden, are we?

THE STAGE MANAGER

Yes, keep straight ahead. You can't miss it. You'll be in Trenton in a few minutes. [*He carefully pours some water into the hood.*] Camden's a great town, lady, believe me.

MA

My daughter likes it fine—my married daughter.

THE STAGE MANAGER

Ye'? It's a great burg all right. I guess I think so because I was born near there.

MA

Well, well. Your folks live there?

THE STAGE MANAGER

No, my old man sold the farm and they built a factory on it. So the folks moved to Philadelphia.

MA

My married daughter Beulah lives there because her husband works in the telephone company.—Stop pokin' me,

Caroline!—We're all going down to see her for a few days.

THE STAGE MANAGER
Ye'?

MA
She's been sick, you see, and I just felt I had to go and see her. My husband and my boy are going to stay at the Y.M.C.A. I hear they've got a dormitory on the top floor that's real clean and comfortable. Had you ever been there?

THE STAGE MANAGER
No. I'm Knights of Columbus myself.

MA
Oh.

THE STAGE MANAGER
I used to play basketball at the Y, though. It looked all right to me. [*He has been standing with one foot on the rung of* MA's *chair. They have taken a great fancy to one another. He reluctantly shakes himself out of it and pretends to examine the car again, whistling.*] Well, I guess you're all set now, lady. I hope you have a good trip; you can't miss it.

EVERYBODY
Thanks. Thanks a lot. Good luck to you.

[*Jolts and lurches.*]

MA
[*With a sigh.*] The world's full of nice people.—That's what I call a nice young man.

CAROLINE
[*Earnestly.*] Ma, you oughtn't to tell'm all everything about yourself.

MA

Well, Caroline, you do your way and I'll do mine.—He looked kinda thin to me. I'd like to feed him up for a few days. His mother lives in Philadelphia and I expect he eats at those dreadful Greek places.

CAROLINE

I'm hungry. Pa, there's a hot-dog stand. K'n I have one?

ELMER

We'll all have one, eh, Kate? We had such an early lunch.

MA

Just as you think best, Elmer.

ELMER

Arthur, here's half a dollar.—Run over and see what they have. Not too much mustard, either.

[ARTHUR *descends from the car and goes off stage right.* MA *and* CAROLINE *get out and walk a bit.*]

MA

What's that flower over there?—I'll take some of those to Beulah.

CAROLINE

It's just a weed, Ma.

MA

I like it.—My, look at the sky, wouldya! I'm glad I was born in New Jersey. I've always said it was the best state in the Union. Every state has something no other state has got.

[*They stroll about humming. Presently* ARTHUR *returns with his hands full of imaginary hot dogs, which he distributes. He is still very much cast down by the recent scandal. He finally approaches his mother and says falteringly.*]

ARTHUR

Ma, I'm sorry. I'm sorry for what I said. [*He bursts into tears and puts his forehead against her elbow.*]

MA

There. There. We all say wicked things at times. I know you didn't mean it like it sounded.

[*He weeps still more violently than before.*]

Why, now, now! I forgive you, Arthur, and tonight before you go to bed you . . . [*She whispers.*] You're a good boy at heart, Arthur, and we all know it.

[CAROLINE *starts to cry too.* MA *is suddenly joyously alive and happy.*]

Sakes alive, it's too nice a day for us all to be cryin'. Come now, get in. You go up in front with your father, Caroline. Ma wants to sit with her beau. I never saw such children. Your hot dogs are all getting wet. Now chew them fine, everybody.—All right, Elmer, forward march.—Caroline, whatever are you doing?

CAROLINE

I'm spitting out the leather, Ma.

MA

Then say "Excuse me."

CAROLINE

Excuse me, please.

MA

What's this place? Arthur, did you see the post office?

ARTHUR

It said Lawrenceville.

MA

Hhn. School kinda nice. I wonder what that big yellow

house set back was.—Now it's beginning to be Trenton.

CAROLINE

Papa, it was near here that George Washington crossed the Delaware. It was near Trenton, Mamma. He was first in war and first in peace and first in the hearts of his countrymen.

MA

[*Surveying the passing world, serene and didactic.*] Well, the thing I like about him best was that he never told a lie.

[*The children are duly cast down. There is a pause.*]

There's a sunset for you. There's nothing like a good sunset.

ARTHUR

There's an Ohio license in front of us. Ma, have you ever been to Ohio?

MA

No.

[*A dreamy silence descends upon them.* CAROLINE *sits closer to her father.* MA *puts her arm around* ARTHUR.]

ARTHUR

Ma, what a lotta people there are in the world, Ma. There must be thousands and thousands in the United States. Ma, how many are there?

MA

I don't know. Ask your father.

ARTHUR

Pa, how many are there?

ELMER

There are a hundred and twenty-six million, Kate.

M A

[*Giving a pressure about* ARTHUR'S *shoulder.*] And they all like to drive out in the evening with their children be-side'm. [*Another pause.*] Why doesn't somebody sing something? Arthur, you're always singing something; what's the matter with you?

ARTHUR

All right. What'll we sing? [*He sketches.*]

> In the Blue Ridge mountains of Virginia,
> On the trail of the lonesome pine . . .

No, I don't like that any more. Let's do:

> I been workin' on de railroad
> All de liblong day.
> I been workin' on de railroad
> Just to pass de time away.

[CAROLINE *joins in at once. Finally even* MA *is singing. Even* PA *is singing.* MA *suddenly jumps up with a wild cry.*]

M A

Elmer, that signpost said Camden, I saw it.

ELMER

All right, Kate, if you're sure.

[*Much shifting of gears, backing, and jolting.*]

M A

Yes, there it is. Camden—five miles. Dear old Beulah.— Now, children, you be good and quiet during dinner. She's just got out of bed after a big sorta operation, and we must all move around kinda quiet. First you drop me and Caroline at the door and just say hello, and then you men-folk go over to the Y.M.C.A. and come back for dinner in about an hour.

CAROLINE

[*Shutting her eyes and pressing her fists passionately against her nose.*] I see the first star. Everybody make a wish.

> Star light, star bright,
> First star I seen tonight.
> I wish I may, I wish I might
> Have the wish I wish tonight.

[*Then solemnly.*] Pins. Mamma, you say "needles." [*She interlocks little fingers with her mother.*]

MA

Needles.

CAROLINE

Shakespeare. Ma, you say "Longfellow."

MA

Longfellow.

CAROLINE

Now it's a secret and I can't tell it to anybody. Ma, you make a wish.

MA

[*With almost grim humor.*] No, I can make wishes without waiting for no star. And I can tell my wishes right out loud too. Do you want to hear them?

CAROLINE

[*Resignedly.*] No, Ma, we know'm already. We've heard'm. [*She hangs her head affectedly on her left shoulder and says with unmalicious mimicry.*] You want me to be a good girl and you want Arthur to be honest-in-word-and-deed.

MA

[*Majestically.*] Yes. So mind yourself.

ELMER

Caroline, take out that letter from Beulah in my coat pocket by you and read aloud the places I marked with red pencil.

CAROLINE

[*Working.*] *"A few blocks after you pass the two big oil tanks on your left . . ."*

EVERYBODY

[*Pointing backward.*] There they are!

CAROLINE

". . . you come to a corner where there's an A and P store on the left and a firehouse kitty-corner to it . . .

[*They all jubilantly identify these landmarks.*]

. . . turn right, go two blocks, and our house is Weyerhauser St. Number 471."

MA

It's an even nicer street than they used to live in. And right handy to an A and P.

CAROLINE

[*Whispering.*] Ma, it's better than our street. It's richer than our street.—Ma, isn't Beulah richer than we are?

MA

[*Looking at her with a firm and glassy eye.*] Mind yourself, missy. I don't want to hear anybody talking about rich or not rich when I'm around. If people aren't nice I don't care how rich they are. I live in the best street in the world because my husband and children live there. [*She glares impressively at* CAROLINE *a moment to let this lesson sink in, then looks up, sees* BEULAH *and waves.*] There's Beulah standing on the steps lookin' for us.

[BEULAH *has appeared and is waving. They all call out:* "Hello, Beulah—Hello." *Presently they are all getting out of the car.* BEULAH *kisses her father long and affectionately.*]

BEULAH

Hello, Papa. Good old Papa. You look tired, Pa.—Hello, Mamma.—Lookit how Arthur and Caroline are growing!

MA

They're bursting all their clothes!—Yes, your pa needs a rest. Thank heaven his vacation has come just now. We'll feed him up and let him sleep late. Pa has a present for you, Loolie. He would go and buy it.

BEULAH

Why, Pa, you're terrible to go and buy anything for me. Isn't he terrible?

MA

Well, it's a secret. You can open it at dinner.

ELMER

Where's Horace, Loolie?

BEULAH

He was kep' over a little at the office. He'll be here any minute. He's crazy to see you all.

MA

All right. You men go over to the Y and come back in about an hour.

BEULAH

[*As her father returns to the wheel, stands out in the street beside him.*] Go straight along, Pa, you can't miss it. It just stares at yuh. [*She puts her arm around his neck and rubs her nose against his temple.*] Crazy old Pa, goin' buyin' things! It's me that ought to be buyin' things for you, Pa.

ELMER
Oh no! There's only one Loolie in the world.

BEULAH
[*Whispering, as her eyes fill with tears.*] Are you glad I'm still alive, Pa?

[*She kisses him abruptly and goes back to the house steps.* THE STAGE MANAGER *removes the automobile with the help of* ELMER *and* ARTHUR, *who go off waving their good-bys.*]

Well, come on upstairs, Ma, and take off your things. Caroline, there's a surprise for you in the back yard.

CAROLINE
Rabbits?

BEULAH
No.

CAROLINE
Chickins?

BEULAH
No. Go and see.

[CAROLINE *runs off stage.* BEULAH *and* MA *gradually go upstairs.*]

There are two new puppies. You be thinking over whether you can keep one in Newark.

MA
I guess we can. It's a nice house, Beulah. You just got a *lovely* home.

BEULAH
When I got back from the hospital, Horace had moved everything into it, and there wasn't anything for me to do.

MA

It's lovely.

[THE STAGE MANAGER *pushes out a bed from the left.
Its foot is toward the right.* BEULAH *sits on it, testing the
springs.*]

BEULAH

I think you'll find the bed comfortable, Ma.

MA

[*Taking off her hat.*] Oh, I could sleep on a heapa shoes,
Loolie! I don't have no trouble sleepin'. [*She sits down
beside her.*] Now let me look at my girl. Well, well, when
I last saw you, you didn't know me. You kep' saying:
"When's Mamma comin'? When's Mamma comin'?"
But the doctor sent me away.

BEULAH

[*Puts her head on her mother's shoulder and weeps.*] It
was awful, Mamma. It was awful. She didn't even live a
few minutes, Mamma. It was awful.

MA

[*Looking far away.*] God thought best, dear. God thought
best. We don't understand why. We just go on, honey,
doin' our business. [*Then almost abruptly—passing the
back of her hand across her cheek.*] Well, now, what are
we giving the men to eat tonight?

BEULAH

There's a chicken in the oven.

MA

What time didya put it in?

BEULAH

[*Restraining her.*] Aw, Ma, don't go yet. I like to sit here
with you this way. You always get the fidgets when we
try and pet yuh, Mamma.

M A

[*Ruefully, laughing.*] Yes, it's kinda foolish. I'm just an old Newark bag o' bones. [*She glances at the backs of her hands.*]

B E U L A H

[*Indignantly.*] Why, Ma, you're good-lookin'! We always said you were good-lookin'.—And besides, you're the best ma we could ever have.

M A

[*Uncomfortable.*] Well, I hope you like me. There's nothin' like being liked by your family.—Now I'm going downstairs to look at the chicken. You stretch out here for a minute and shut your eyes.—Have you got everything laid in for breakfast before the shops close?

B E U L A H

Oh, you know! Ham and eggs.

[*They both laugh.*]

M A

I declare I never could understand what men see in ham and eggs. I think they're horrible.—What time did you put the chicken in?

B E U L A H

Five o'clock.

M A

Well, now, you shut your eyes for ten minutes.

[B E U L A H *stretches out and shuts her eyes.* M A *descends the stairs absent-mindedly singing.*]

There were ninety and nine that safely lay
In the shelter of the fold,
But one was out on the hills away,
Far off from the gates of gold. . . .

SUPPRESSED DESIRES

A Comedy

By Susan Glaspell

in collaboration with
George Cram Cook

CAST

Henrietta Brewster
Stephen Brewster
Mabel

SCENE I: *A studio apartment in an upper story, Washington Square South. Through an immense north window in the back wall appear tree tops and the upper part of the Washington Arch. Beyond it you look up Fifth Avenue. Near the window is a big table, loaded at one end with serious-looking books and austere scientific periodicals. At the other end are architect's drawings, blue prints, dividing compasses, square, ruler, etc. At the left is a door leading to the rest of the apartment; at the right the outer door. A breakfast table is set for three, but only two are seated at it*—HENRIETTA *and* STEPHEN BREWSTER. *As the curtains withdraw* STEVE *pushes back his coffee cup and sits dejected.*

H E N R I E T T A

It isn't the coffee, Steve dear. There's nothing the matter with the coffee. There's something the matter with *you.*

S T E V E

[*Doggedly.*] There may be something the matter with my stomach.

H E N R I E T T A

[*Scornfully.*] Your stomach! The trouble is not with your stomach but in your subconscious mind.

S T E V E

Subconscious piffle! [*Takes morning paper and tries to read.*]

H E N R I E T T A

Steve, you never used to be so disagreeable. You certainly

have got some sort of a complex. You're all inhibited.
You're no longer open to new ideas. You won't listen to a
word about psychoanalysis.

STEVE

A word! I've listened to volumes!

HENRIETTA

You've ceased to be creative in architecture—your work
isn't going well. You're not sleeping well——

STEVE

How can I sleep, Henrietta, when you're always waking
me up to find out what I'm dreaming?

HENRIETTA

But dreams are so important, Steve. If you'd tell yours to
Dr. Russell he'd find out exactly what's wrong with you.

STEVE

There's nothing wrong with me.

HENRIETTA

You don't even talk as well as you used to.

STEVE

Talk? I can't say a thing without you looking at me in
that dark fashion you have when you're on the trail of a
complex.

HENRIETTA

This very irritability indicates that you're suffering from
some suppressed desire.

STEVE

I'm suffering from a suppressed desire for a little peace.

HENRIETTA

Dr. Russell is doing simply wonderful things with nervous
cases. Won't you go to him, Steve?

STEVE
[*Slamming down his newspaper.*] No, Henrietta, I won't!

HENRIETTA
But Stephen——!

STEVE
Tst! I hear Mabel coming. Let's not be at each other's throats the first day of her visit.

[*He takes out cigarettes.* MABEL *comes in from door left, the side opposite* STEVE, *so that he is facing her. She is wearing a rather fussy negligee in contrast to* HENRIETTA, *who wears "radical" clothes.* MABEL *is what is called plump.*]

MABEL
Good morning.

HENRIETTA
Oh, here you are, little sister.

STEVE
Good morning, Mabel.

[MABEL *nods to him and turns, her face lighting up, to* HENRIETTA.]

HENRIETTA
[*Giving* MABEL *a hug as she leans against her.*] It's so good to have you here. I was going to let you sleep, thinking you'd be tired after the long trip. Sit down. There'll be fresh toast in a minute and [*Rising.*] will you have——

MABEL
Oh, I ought to have told you, Henrietta. Don't get anything for me. I'm not eating breakfast.

HENRIETTA
[*At first in mere surprise.*] Not eating breakfast? [*She sits*

down, then leans toward MABEL *who is seated now, and scrutinizes her.*]

STEVE
[*Half to himself.*] The psychoanalytical look!

HENRIETTA
Mabel, why are you not eating breakfast?

MABEL
[*A little startled.*] Why, no particular reason. I just don't care much for breakfast, and they say it keeps down—— [*A hand on her hip—the gesture of one who is reducing.*] that is, it's a good thing to go without it.

HENRIETTA
Don't you sleep well? Did you sleep well last night?

MABEL
Oh, yes, I slept all right. Yes, I slept fine last night, only [*Laughing.*] I did have the funniest dream!

STEVE
S-h! S-t!

HENRIETTA
[*Moving closer.*] And what did you dream, Mabel?

STEVE
Look-a-here, Mabel, I feel it's my duty to put you on. Don't tell Henrietta your dreams. If you do she'll find out that you have an underground desire to kill your father and marry your mother——

HENRIETTA
Don't be absurd, Stephen Brewster. [*Sweetly to* MABEL.] What was your dream, dear?

MABEL
[*Laughing.*] Well, I dreamed I was a hen.

HENRIETTA
A hen?

MABEL
Yes; and I was pushing along through a crowd as fast as I could, but being a hen I couldn't walk very fast—it was like having a tight skirt, you know; and there was some sort of creature in a blue cap—you know how mixed up dreams are—and it kept shouting after me, "Step, Hen! Step, Hen!" until I got all excited and just couldn't move at all.

HENRIETTA
[*Resting chin in palm and peering.*] You say you became much excited?

MABEL
[*Laughing.*] Oh, yes; I was in a terrible state.

HENRIETTA
[*Leaning back, murmurs.*] This is significant.

STEVE
She dreams she's a hen. She is told to step lively. She becomes violently agitated. What can it mean?

HENRIETTA
[*Turning impatiently from him.*] Mabel, do you know anything about psychoanalysis?

MABEL
[*Feebly.*] Oh—not much. No—I—— [*Brightening.*] It's something about the war, isn't it?

STEVE
Not that kind of war.

MABEL
[*Abashed.*] I thought it might be the name of a new explosive.

STEVE
It *is.*

MABEL
[*Apologetically to* HENRIETTA, *who is frowning.*] You see, Henrietta, I—we do not live in touch with intellectual things, as you do. Bob being a dentist—somehow our friends——

STEVE
[*Softly.*] Oh, to be a dentist! [*Goes to window and stands looking out.*]

HENRIETTA
Don't you see anything more of that editorial writer—what was his name?

MABEL
Lyman Eggleston?

HENRIETTA
Yes, Eggleston. He was in touch with things. Don't you see him?

MABEL
Yes, I see him once in a while. Bob doesn't like him very well.

HENRIETTA
Your husband does not like Lyman Eggleston? [*Mysteriously.*] Mabel, are you perfectly happy with your husband?

STEVE
[*Sharply.*] Oh, come now, Henrietta—that's going a little strong!

HENRIETTA
Are you perfectly happy with him, Mabel?

[STEVE *goes to work-table.*]

MABEL

Why—yes—I guess so. Why——of course I am!

HENRIETTA

Are you happy? Or do you only think you are? Or do you only think you *ought* to be?

MABEL

Why, Henrietta, I don't know what you mean!

STEVE

[*Seizes stack of books and magazines and dumps them on the breakfast table.*] This is what she means, Mabel. Psychoanalysis. My work-table groans with it. Books by Freud, the new Messiah; books by Jung, the new St. Paul; the Psychoanalytical Review—back numbers two-fifty per.

MABEL

But what's it all about?

STEVE

All about your sub-un-non-conscious mind and desires you know not of. They may be doing you a great deal of harm. You may go crazy with them. Oh, yes! People are doing it right and left. Your dreaming you're a hen—— [*Shakes his head darkly.*]

HENRIETTA

Any fool can ridicule anything.

MABEL

[*Hastily, to avert a quarrel.*] But what do you say it is, Henrietta?

STEVE

[*Looking at his watch.*] Oh, if Henrietta's going to start that! [*During* HENRIETTA'S *next speech settles himself at work-table and sharpens a lead pencil.*]

HENRIETTA

It's like this, Mabel. You want something. You think you

can't have it. You think it's wrong. So you try to think you don't want it. Your mind protects you—avoids pain—by refusing to think the forbidden thing. But it's there just the same. It stays there shut up in your unconscious mind, and it festers.

STEVE

Sort of an ingrowing mental toenail.

HENRIETTA

Precisely. The forbidden impulse is there full of energy which has simply got to do something. It breaks into your consciousness in disguise, masks itself in dreams, makes all sorts of trouble. In extreme cases it drives you insane.

MABEL

[*With a gesture of horror.*] Oh!

HENRIETTA

[*Reassuring.*] But psychoanalysis has found out how to save us from that. It brings into consciousness the suppressed desire that was making all the trouble. Psychoanalysis is simply the latest scientific method of preventing and curing insanity.

STEVE

[*From his table.*] It is also the latest scientific method of separating families.

HENRIETTA

[*Mildly.*] Families that ought to be separated.

STEVE

The Dwights, for instance. You must have met them, Mabel, when you were here before. Helen was living, apparently, in peace and happiness with good old Joe. Well—she went to this psychoanalyzer—she was "psyched," and biff!—bang!—home she comes with an unsuppressed desire to leave her husband. [*He starts work, drawing lines on a drawing board with a T-square.*]

MABEL

How terrible! Yes, I remember Helen Dwight. But—but did she have such a desire?

STEVE

First she'd known of it.

MABEL

And she *left* him?

HENRIETTA

[*Coolly.*] Yes, she did.

MABEL

Wasn't he good to her?

HENRIETTA

Why, yes, good enough.

MABEL

Wasn't he kind to her?

HENRIETTA

Oh, yes——kind to her.

MABEL

And she left her good, kind husband——!

HENRIETTA

Oh, Mabel! "Left her good, kind husband!" How naïve ——forgive me, dear, but how bourgeois you are! She came to know herself. And she had the courage!

MABEL

I may be very naïve and—bourgeois—but I don't see the good of a new science that breaks up homes.

[STEVE *applauds.*]

STEVE

In enlightening Mabel, we mustn't neglect to mention

the case of Art Holden's private secretary, Mary Snow, who has just been informed of her suppressed desire for her employer.

MABEL
Why, I think it is terrible, Henrietta! It would be better if we didn't know such things about ourselves.

HENRIETTA
No, Mabel, that is the old way.

MABEL
But—but her employer? Is he married?

STEVE
[*Grunts.*] Wife and four children.

MABEL
Well, then, what good does it do the girl to be told she has a desire for him? There's nothing can be done about it.

HENRIETTA
Old institutions will have to be reshaped so that something can be done in such cases. It happens, Mabel, that this suppressed desire was on the point of landing Mary Snow in the insane asylum. Are you so tight-minded that you'd rather have her in the insane asylum than break the conventions?

MABEL
But—but have people always had these awful suppressed desires?

HENRIETTA
Always.

STEVE
But they've just been discovered.

HENRIETTA
The harm they do has just been discovered. And free, sane people must face the fact that they have to be dealt with.

MABEL

[*Stoutly.*] I don't believe they have them in Chicago.

HENRIETTA

[*Business of giving* MABEL *up.*] People "have them" wherever the living Libido—the center of the soul's energy—is in conflict with petrified moral codes. That means everywhere in civilization. Psychoanalysis——

STEVE

Good God! I've got the roof in the cellar!

HENRIETTA

The roof in the cellar!

STEVE

[*Holding plan at arm's length.*] That's what psychoanalysis does!

HENRIETTA

That's what psychoanalysis could *un*-do. Is it any wonder I'm concerned about Steve? He dreamed the other night that the walls of his room melted away and he found himself alone in a forest. Don't you see how significant it is for an architect to have *walls* slip away from him? It symbolizes his loss of grip in his work. There's some suppressed desire——

STEVE

[*Hurling his ruined plan viciously to the floor.*] Suppressed hell!

HENRIETTA

You speak more truly than you know. It is through suppressions that hells are formed in us.

MABEL

[*Looking at* STEVE, *who is tearing his hair.*] Don't you think it would be a good thing, Henrietta, if we went somewhere else?

[*They rise and begin to pick up the dishes.* MABEL *drops a plate which breaks.* HENRIETTA *draws up short and looks at her—the psychoanalytic look.*]

I'm sorry, Henrietta. One of the Spode plates, too. [*Surprised and resentful as* HENRIETTA *continues to peer at her.*] Don't take it so to heart, Henrietta.

HENRIETTA
I can't help taking it to heart.

MABEL
I'll get you another. [*Pause. More sharply as* HENRIETTA *does not answer.*] I said I'll get you another plate, Henrietta.

HENRIETTA
It's not the plate.

MABEL
For heaven's sake, what is it then?

HENRIETTA
It's the significant little false movement that made you drop it.

MABEL
Well, I suppose everyone makes a false movement once in a while.

HENRIETTA
Yes, Mabel, but these false movements all mean something.

MABEL
[*About to cry.*] I don't think that's very nice! It was just because I happened to think of that Mabel Snow you were talking about——

HENRIETTA
Mabel Snow!

MABEL

Snow—Snow—well, what was her name, then?

HENRIETTA

Her name is Mary. You substituted *your own* name for hers.

MABEL

Well, *Mary* Snow, then; *Mary* Snow. I never heard her name but once. I don't see anything to make such a fuss about.

HENRIETTA

[*Gently.*] Mabel dear—mistakes like that in names——

MABEL

[*Desperately.*] They don't mean something, too, do they?

HENRIETTA

[*Gently.*] I am sorry, dear, but they do.

MABEL

But I'm always doing that!

HENRIETTA

[*After a start of horror.*] My poor little sister, tell me about it.

MABEL

About what?

HENRIETTA

About your not being happy. About your longing for another sort of life.

MABEL

But I *don't.*

HENRIETTA

Ah, I understand these things, dear. You feel Bob is limiting you to a life in which you do not feel free——

MABEL

Henrietta! When did I ever say such a thing?

HENRIETTA

You said you are not in touch with things intellectual. You showed your feeling that it is Bob's profession—that has engendered a resentment which has colored your whole life with him.

MABEL

Why—Henrietta!

HENRIETTA

Don't be afraid of me, little sister. There's nothing can shock me or turn me from you. I am not like that. I wanted you to come for this visit because I had a feeling that you needed more from life than you were getting. No one of these things I have seen would excite my suspicion. It's the combination. You don't eat breakfast [*Enumerating on her fingers.*] You make false moves; you substitute your own name for the name of another *whose love is misdirected*. You're nervous; you *look* queer; in your eyes there's a frightened look that is most unlike you. And this dream. A *hen*. Come with me this afternoon to Dr. Russell! Your whole life may be at stake, Mabel.

MABEL

[*Gasping.*] Henrietta, I—you—you always were the smartest in the family, and all that, but—this is terrible! I don't think we *ought* to think such things. [*Brightening.*] Why, I'll tell you why I dreamed I was a hen. It was because last night, telling about that time in Chicago, you said I was as mad as a wet hen.

HENRIETTA

[*Superior.*] Did you dream you were a *wet* hen?

MABEL

[*Forced to admit it.*] No.

HENRIETTA

No. You dreamed you were a *dry* hen. And why, being a hen, were you urged to step?

MABEL

Maybe it's because when I am getting on a street car it always irritates me to have them call "Step lively."

HENRIETTA

No, Mabel, that is only a child's view of it—if you will forgive me. You see merely the elements used in the dream. You do not see into the dream; you do not see its meaning. This dream of the hen——

STEVE

Hen—hen—wet hen—dry hen—mad hen! [*Jumps up in a rage.*] Let me out of this!

HENRIETTA

[*Hastily picking up dishes, speaks soothingly.*] Just a minute, dear, and we'll have things so you can work in quiet. Mabel and I are going to sit in my room. [*She goes out left, carrying dishes.*]

STEVE

[*Seizing hat and coat from an alcove near the outside door.*] I'm going to be psychoanalyzed. I'm going now! I'm going straight to that infallible doctor of hers—that priest of this new religion. If he's got honesty enough to tell Henrietta there's nothing the matter with my unconscious mind, perhaps I can be let alone about it, and then I *will* be all right. [*From the door in a loud voice.*] Don't tell Henrietta I'm going. It might take weeks, and I couldn't stand all the talk. [*He hurries out.*]

HENRIETTA

[*Returning.*] Where's Steve? Gone? [*With a hopeless gesture.*] You see how impatient he is—how unlike himself! I tell you, Mabel, I'm nearly distracted about Steve.

MABEL

I think he's a little distracted, too.

HENRIETTA

Well, if he's gone—you might as well stay here. I have a committee meeting at the bookshop, and will have to leave you to yourself for an hour or two. [*As she puts her hat on, taking it from the alcove where* STEVE *found his, her eye, lighting up almost carnivorously, falls on an enormous volume on the floor beside the work-table. The book has been half hidden by the wastebasket. She picks it up and carries it around the table toward* MABEL.] Here, dear, is one of the simplest statements of psychoanalysis. You just read this and then we can talk more intelligently.

[MABEL *takes volume and staggers back under its weight to chair rear center,* HENRIETTA *goes to outer door, stops and asks abruptly.*]

How old is Lyman Eggleston?

MABEL

[*Promptly.*] He isn't forty yet. Why, what made you ask that, Henrietta? [*As she turns her head to look at* HENRIETTA *her hands move toward the upper corners of the book balanced on her knees.*]

HENRIETTA

Oh, nothing. Au revoir.

[*She goes out.* MABEL *stares at the ceiling. The book slides to the floor. She starts; looks at the book, then at the broken plate on the table.*]

MABEL

The plate! The book! [*She lifts her eyes, leans forward, elbow on knee, chin on knuckles and plaintively queries.*] Am I unhappy?

CURTAIN

SCENE II: *Two weeks later. The stage is as in Scene I, except that the breakfast table has been removed. During the first few minutes the dusk of a winter afternoon deepens. Out of the darkness spring rows of double street-lights almost meeting in the distance.* HENRIETTA *is at the psychoanalytical end of* STEVE'S *work-table, surrounded by open books and periodicals, writing.* STEVE *enters briskly.*

STEVE

What are you doing, my dear?

HENRIETTA

My paper for the Liberal Club.

STEVE

Your paper on——?

HENRIETTA

On a subject which does not have your sympathy.

STEVE

Oh, I'm not sure I'm wholly out of sympathy with psychoanalysis, Henrietta. You worked it so hard. I couldn't even take a bath without its meaning something.

HENRIETTA

[*Loftily.*] I talked it because I knew you needed it.

STEVE

You haven't said much about it these last two weeks. Uh—your faith in it hasn't weakened any?

HENRIETTA

Weakened? It's grown stronger with each new thing I've come to know. And Mabel. She is with Dr. Russell now. Dr. Russell is wonderful! From what Mabel tells me I believe his analysis is going to prove that I was right. Today

I discovered a remarkable confirmation of my theory in the hen-dream.

STEVE
What is your theory?

HENRIETTA
Well, you know about Lyman Eggleston. I've wondered about him. I've never seen him, but I know he's less bourgeois than Mabel's other friends—more intellectual—and [*Significantly.*] she doesn't see much of him because Bob doesn't like him.

STEVE
But what's the confirmation?

HENRIETTA
Today I noticed the first syllable of his name.

STEVE
Ly?

HENRIETTA
No—egg.

STEVE
Egg?

HENRIETTA
[*Patiently.*] Mabel dreamed she was a *hen*. [STEVE *laughs.*] You wouldn't laugh if you knew how important names are in interpreting dreams. Freud is full of just such cases in which a whole hidden complex is revealed by a single significant syllable—like this egg.

STEVE
Doesn't the traditional relation of hen and egg suggest rather a maternal feeling?

HENRIETTA
There is something maternal in Mabel's love, of course,

but that's only one element.

STEVE

Well, suppose Mabel hasn't a suppressed desire to be this gentleman's mother, but his beloved. What's to be done about it? What about Bob? Don't you think it's going to be a little rough on him?

HENRIETTA

That can't be helped. Bob, like everyone else, must face the facts of life. If Dr. Russell should arrive independently at this same interpretation I shall not hesitate to advise Mabel to leave her present husband.

STEVE

Um—hum! [*The lights go up on Fifth Avenue.* STEVE *goes to the window and looks out.*] How long is it we've lived here, Henrietta?

HENRIETTA

Why, this is the third year, Steve.

STEVE

I—we—one would miss this view if one went away, wouldn't one?

HENRIETTA

How strangely you speak! Oh, Stephen, I *wish* you'd go to Dr. Russell. Don't think my fears have abated because I've been able to restrain myself. I had to on account of Mabel. But now, dear—won't you go?

STEVE

I— [*He breaks off, turns on the light, then comes and sits beside* HENRIETTA.] How long have we been married, Henrietta?

HENRIETTA

Stephen, I don't understand you! You *must* go to Dr. Russell.

STEVE
I have gone.

HENRIETTA
You—what?

STEVE
[*Jauntily.*] Yes, Henrietta, I've been psyched.

HENRIETTA
You went to Dr. Russell?

STEVE
The same.

HENRIETTA
And what did he say?

STEVE
He said—I—I was a little surprised by what he said, Henrietta.

HENRIETTA
[*Breathlessly.*] Of course—one can so seldom anticipate. But tell me—your dream, Stephen? It means——?

STEVE
It means—I was considerably surprised by what it means.

HENRIETTA
Don't be so exasperating!

STEVE
It means—you really want to know, Henrietta?

HENRIETTA
Stephen, you'll drive me mad!

STEVE
He said—of course he may be wrong in what he said.

HENRIETTA
He *isn't* wrong. *Tell* me!

STEVE
He said my dream of the walls receding and leaving me
alone in a forest indicates a suppressed desire——

HENRIETTA
Yes—yes!

STEVE
To be freed from——

HENRIETTA
Yes—freed from——?

STEVE
Marriage.

HENRIETTA
[*Crumples. Stares.*] Marriage!

STEVE
He—he may be mistaken, you know.

HENRIETTA
May be mistaken?

STEVE
I—well, of course, I hadn't taken any stock in it myself.
It was only your great confidence——

HENRIETTA
Stephen, are you telling me that Dr. Russell—Dr. A. E.
Russell—told you this?

[STEVE *nods.*]

Told you you have a suppressed desire to separate from
me?

STEVE
That's what he said.

HENRIETTA
Did he know who you were?

STEVE

Yes.

HENRIETTA

That you were married to me?

STEVE

Yes, he knew that.

HENRIETTA

And he told you to leave me?

STEVE

It seems he must be wrong, Henrietta.

HENRIETTA

[*Rising.*] And I've sent him more patients——! [*Catches herself and resumes coldly.*] What reason did he give for this analysis?

STEVE

He says the confining walls are a symbol of my feeling about marriage and that their fading away is a wish-fulfillment.

HENRIETTA

[*Gulping.*] Well, is it? Do you want our marriage to end?

STEVE

It was a great surprise to me that I did. You see I hadn't known what was in my unconscious mind.

HENRIETTA

[*Flaming.*] What did you tell Dr. Russell about me to make him think you weren't happy?

STEVE

I never told him a thing, Henrietta. He got it all from his confounded clever inferences. I—I tried to refute them, but he said that was only part of my self-protective lying.

HENRIETTA

And that's why you were so—happy—when you came in just now!

STEVE

Why, Henrietta, how can you say such a thing? I was *sad*. Didn't I speak sadly of—of the view? Didn't I ask how long we had been married?

HENRIETTA

[*Rising.*] Stephen Brewster, have you no sense of the seriousness of this? Dr. Russell doesn't know what our marriage has been. You do. You should have laughed him down! Confined—in life with me? Did you tell him that I *believe* in freedom?

STEVE

I very emphatically told him that his results were a great surprise to me.

HENRIETTA

But you accepted them.

STEVE

Oh, not at all. I merely couldn't refute his arguments. I'm not a psychologist. I came home to talk it over with you. You being a disciple of psychoanalysis——

HENRIETTA

If you are going, I wish you would go tonight!

STEVE

Oh, my dear! I—surely I couldn't do that! Think of my feelings. And my laundry hasn't come home.

HENRIETTA

I ask you to go tonight. Some women would falter at this, Steve, but I am not such a woman. I leave you free. I do not repudiate psychoanalysis; I say again that it has done great things. It has also made mistakes, of course. But since you accept this analysis— [*She sits down and pretends to begin work.*] I have to finish this paper. I wish you would leave me.

STEVE

[*Scratches his head, goes to the inner door.*] I'm sorry, Henrietta, about my unconscious mind.

[*Alone,* HENRIETTA'*s face betrays her outraged state of mind—disconcerted, resentful, trying to pull herself together. She attains an air of bravely bearing an outrageous thing. The outer door opens and* MABEL *enters in great excitement.*]

MABEL

[*Breathless.*] Henrietta, I'm so glad you're here. And alone? [*Looks toward the inner door.*] Are you alone, Henrietta?

HENRIETTA

[*With reproving dignity.*] Very much so.

MABEL

[*Rushing to her.*] Henrietta, he's found it!

HENRIETTA

[*Aloof.*] Who has found what?

MABEL

Who has found what? Dr. Russell has found my suppressed desire!

HENRIETTA

That is interesting.

MABEL

He finished with me today—he got hold of my complex— in the most amazing way! But, oh, Henrietta—it is so terrible!

HENRIETTA

Do calm yourself, Mabel. Surely there's no occasion for all this agitation.

MABEL

But there is! And when you think of the lives that are affected—the readjustments that must be made in order to bring the suppressed hell out of me and save me from the insane asylum——!

HENRIETTA

The insane asylum!

MABEL

You said that's where these complexes brought people!

HENRIETTA

What did the doctor tell you, Mabel?

MABEL

Oh, I don't know how I can tell you—it is so awful—so unbelievable.

HENRIETTA

I rather have my hand in at hearing the unbelievable.

MABEL

Henrietta, who would ever have thought it? How can it be true? But the doctor is perfectly certain that I have a suppressed desire for—— [*Looks at* HENRIETTA, *is unable to continue.*]

HENRIETTA

Oh, go on, Mabel. I'm not unprepared for what you have to say.

MABEL

Not unprepared? You mean you have suspected it?

HENRIETTA

From the first. It's been my theory all along.

MABEL

But, Henrietta, I didn't know myself that I had this secret desire for Stephen.

HENRIETTA

[*Jumps up.*] Stephen!

MABEL

My brother-in-law! My own sister's husband!

HENRIETTA

You have a suppressed desire for *Stephen!*

MABEL

Oh, Henrietta, aren't these unconscious selves terrible? They seem so unlike *us!*

HENRIETTA

What insane thing are you driving at?

MABEL

[*Blubbering.*] Henrietta, don't you use that word to me. I don't *want* to go to the insane asylum.

HENRIETTA

What did Dr. Russell say?

MABEL

Well, you see—oh, it's the strangest thing! But you know the voice in my dream that called "Step, Hen!" Dr. Russell found out today that when I was a little girl I had a story-book in words of one syllable and I read the name Stephen wrong. I used to read it S-t-e-p, step, h-e-n, hen. [*Dramatically.*] Step Hen is Stephen.

[*Enter* STEPHEN, *his head bent over a time-table.*]

Stephen is Step Hen!

STEVE

I? Step Hen?

MABEL

[*Triumphantly.*] S-t-e-p, step, H-e-n, hen, Stephen!

HENRIETTA

[*Exploding.*] Well, what if Stephen is Step Hen? [*Scornfully.*] Step Hen! Step Hen! For that ridiculous coincidence——

MABEL

Coincidence! But it's childish to look at the mere elements of a dream. You have to look *into* it—you have to see what it *means!*

HENRIETTA

On account of that trivial, meaningless play on syllables—on that flimsy basis—you are ready—— [*Wails.*] O-h!

STEVE

What on earth's the matter? What has happened? Suppose I *am* Step Hen? What about it? What does it mean?

MABEL

[*Crying.*] It means—that I—have a suppressed desire for *you!*

STEVE

For me! The deuce you have! [*Feebly.*] What—er—makes you think so?

MABEL

Dr. Russell has worked it out scientifically.

HENRIETTA

Yes. Through the amazing discovery that Step Hen equals Stephen!

MABEL

[*Tearfully.*] Oh, that isn't all—that isn't near all. Henrietta won't give me a chance to tell it. She'd rather I'd go to the insane asylum than be unconventional.

HENRIETTA

We'll all go there if you can't control yourself. We are still waiting for some rational report.

MABEL

[*Drying her eyes.*] Oh, there's such a lot about names. [*With some pride.*] I don't see how I ever did it. It all works in together. I dreamed I was a hen because that's the first syllable of *Hen*rietta's name, and when I dreamed I was a hen, I was putting myself in Henrietta's place.

HENRIETTA

With Stephen?

MABEL

With Stephen.

HENRIETTA

[*Outraged.*] Oh!

[*Turns in rage upon* STEPHEN, *who is fanning himself with the time-table.*]

What are you doing with that time-table?

STEVE

Why—I thought—you were so keen to have me go tonight —I thought I'd just take a run up to Canada, and join Billy—a little shooting—but——

MABEL

But there's more about the names.

HENRIETTA

Mabel, have you thought of Bob—dear old Bob—your good, kind husband?

MABEL

Oh, Henrietta, "my good, kind husband!"

HENRIETTA

Think of him, Mabel, out there alone in Chicago, working his head off, fixing people's *teeth*—for you!

MABEL

Yes, but think of the living Libido—in conflict with petrified moral codes! And think of the perfectly wonderful
way the names all prove it. Dr. Russell said he's never
seen anything more convincing. Just look at Stephen's
last name—Brewster. I dream I'm a hen, and the name
Brewster—you have to say its first letter by itself—and
then the hen, that's me, she says to him: "Stephen, Be
Rooster!"

[HENRIETTA *and* STEPHEN *collapse into the nearest
chairs.*]

MABEL

I think it's perfectly wonderful! Why, if it wasn't for
psychoanalysis you'd never find out how wonderful your
own mind is!

STEVE

[*Begins to chuckle.*] Be Rooster! Stephen, Be Rooster!

HENRIETTA

You think it's funny, do you?

STEVE

Well, what's to be done about it? Does Mabel have to go
away with me?

HENRIETTA

Do you want Mabel to go away with you?

STEVE

Well, but Mabel herself—her complex, her suppressed
desire——!

HENRIETTA

[*Going to her.*] Mabel, are you going to insist on going
away with Stephen?

MABEL

I'd rather go with Stephen than go to the insane asylum!

HENRIETTA

For heaven's sake, Mabel, drop that insane asylum! If you *did* have a suppressed desire for Stephen hidden away in you—God knows it isn't hidden now. Dr. Russell has brought it into your consciousness—with a vengeance. That's all that's necessary to break up a complex. Psychoanalysis doesn't say you have to *gratify* every suppressed desire.

STEVE

[*Softly.*] Unless it's for Lyman Eggleston.

HENRIETTA

[*Turning on him.*] Well, if it comes to that, Stephen Brewster, I'd like to know why that interpretation of mine isn't as good as this one? Step, Hen!

STEVE

But Be Rooster! [*He pauses, chuckling to himself.*] Step-Hen Be rooster. And *H*enrietta. Pshaw, my dear, Doc Russell's got you beat a mile! [*He turns away and chuckles.*] Be rooster!

MABEL

What has Lyman Eggleston got to do with it?

STEVE

According to Henrietta, you, the hen, have a suppressed desire for *Egg*leston, the egg.

MABEL

Henrietta, I think that's indecent of you! He is bald as an egg and little and fat—the idea of you thinking such a thing of me!

HENRIETTA

Well, Bob isn't little and bald and fat! Why don't you stick to your own husband? [*To* STEPHEN.] What if Dr.

Russell's interpretation has got mine "beat a mile"? [*Resentful look at him.*] It would only mean that Mabel doesn't want Eggleston and does want you. Does that mean she has to have you?

MABEL

But you said Mabel Snow——

HENRIETTA

Mary Snow! You're not as much like her as you think—substituting your name for hers! The cases are entirely different. Oh, I wouldn't have *believed* this of you, Mabel. [*Beginning to cry.*] I brought you here for a pleasant visit—thought you needed brightening *up*—wanted to be *nice* to you—and now you—my husband—you insist—— [*In fumbling her way to her chair she brushes to the floor some sheets from the psychoanalytical table.*]

STEVE

[*With solicitude.*] Careful, dear. Your paper on psychoanalysis! [*Gathers up sheets and offers them to her.*]

HENRIETTA

I don't want my paper on psychoanalysis! I'm sick of psychoanalysis!

STEVE

[*Eagerly.*] Do you mean that, Henrietta?

HENRIETTA

Why shouldn't I mean it? Look at all I've done for psychoanalysis—and— [*Raising a tear-stained face.*] What has psychoanalysis done for me?

STEVE

Do you mean, Henrietta, that you're going to stop *talking* psychoanalysis?

HENRIETTA

Why shouldn't I stop talking it? Haven't I seen what it does to people? Mabel has gone crazy about psychoanalysis!

[*At the word "crazy" with a moan* MABEL *sinks to chair and buries her face in her hands.*]

STEVE

[*Solemnly.*] Do you swear never to wake me up in the night to find out what I'm dreaming?

HENRIETTA

Dream what you please—I don't care what you're dreaming.

STEVE

Will you clear off my work-table so the Journal of Morbid Psychology doesn't stare me in the face when I'm trying to plan a house?

HENRIETTA

[*Pushing a stack of periodicals off the table.*] I'll *burn* the Journal of Morbid Psychology!

STEVE

My dear Henrietta, if you're going to separate from psychoanalysis, there's no reason why I should separate from *you.*

[*They embrace ardently.* MABEL *lifts her head and looks at them woefully.*]

MABEL

[*Jumping up and going toward them.*] But what about me? What am I to do with my suppressed desire?

STEVE

[*With one arm still around* HENRIETTA, *gives* MABEL *a brotherly hug.*] Mabel, you just keep right on suppressing it!

THE TRIUMPH
OF THE EGG

By Sherwood Anderson

CAST

Mother
Father
Joe Kane
Freddie, a small child
Commuters

*This play is a slice of life, between the arrival of two com-
muter trains. The scene reveals a stage divided into two
sections. The larger, on the right, is the restaurant. There
is an entrance in the back wall, to the right. It is summer,
and only the screen door across the entrance is closed. In
the back wall, about center, is a large window, through
which the street and a street lamp can be dimly seen. A
shaded, hanging oil lamp lights the room. Along the right
wall, well down stage, are two small tables with straight
chairs above and below them. They are covered with linen,
none too white, and the usual array of salt and pepper
shakers, mustard jars, ash trays and sugar bowls is on each
table. Back stage, at the side of the window, are shelves,
containing small boxes of cereal, cigars, cigarettes. The
counter runs parallel to the back wall, and is set far enough
out from the wall to allow a person to move about behind
it. The right end of the counter, near the outer door, is
closed, but the left end of the counter, near the bedroom,
is open. There is sufficient room between the left end of the
counter and the door to the bedroom for a person to
move about without difficulty. On the counter are plates
of apples, eggs, and doughnuts, heaped up. Back of the
counter and below it are evidently shelves for dishes, and
a hot plate, where coffee is kept steaming. On the walls are
signs: "We Aim To Please; Eggs Any Style!"*

*The small room to the left is the bedroom. There is an
entrance well up stage, in the skeleton wall slightly at an
angle, which separates the two rooms. Cheap calico hang-
ings, across the wall back stage in the bedroom, seem to*

*hide a makeshift clothes closet frim view. Down stage, the
bed stands with its open iron-work head toward the audience. Up stage, there is a cradle large enough for* FREDDIE.
*There are two straight chairs in the bedroom, and a bat-
tered mirror hanging. There is a small table beneath the
mirror, and a bracket light.*

*While the house lights are still down, before the curtain
rises, there is a train whistle heard, coming afar off from
the right. The curtain rises slowly, and* JOE KANE *can be
seen through the rear window, making his way from left
to right of stage, and coming in at the door. He glances in
the direction of the approaching train, and then, seeing no
one behind the counter, sits down to read his newspaper.*

In the bedroom, the FATHER *is sitting, smoking a pipe,
his chair tipped back against the wall.* FREDDIE *is standing
on the bed, being undressed by the* MOTHER, *who is already
in her nightgown, with her hair hanging down her back.
The* FATHER *pays no attention to her, but smokes, lost in
thought, as she speaks wearily.* FREDDIE *is tired, but patient.*

MOTHER

Well, I don't know. I'm getting pretty tired of it. We've
got to get along somehow; can't always be stick-in-the-
muds. [*To* FREDDIE.] Will you hold still and let me get your
waist off! Always fussin' . . . Suppose we did lose a lot
of time in Bidwell—that doesn't mean anything. We've
got a good start here, and we've got to make something of
it. No use getting discouraged the way you've been here
lately; no use at all. [*To* FREDDIE.] Will you quit playing
with that *button!* You'll have it off in a minute, and then
I'll have to sew it on again. That's the way all of my time
goes—just little things. Now, stop your whimpering, or
I'll give you something to whimper for. Now, shut up!
[*She goes on undressing* FREDDIE.] It's the boy here I'm
worrying about. I don't suppose we'll ever get very far,
you and me. Now, don't think we'll nagging you—it ain't

that; but it just ain't in us. [*To* FREDDIE.] Stop that, now!
Don't you ever let me see you pick your nose again! Shame
on you! [*Pause.*] There ain't any reason why he shouldn't
be *President* if he wants to. Why not? Any American boy
can be President. [*To* FREDDIE.] *Will* you take your finger
out of your nose! Any boy can be President that wants to,
and no matter how poor he is. Look at Lincoln and look
at Garfield! Look how they got clear to the top from
nothing! They didn't have any better chance than Freddie, did they, at the start? And look where they got to!

FATHER

[*Knocking the ashes from his pipe, and speaking thoughtfully, quietly.*] Say, Maw . . .

MOTHER

[*Talking on, unheeding.*] Poverty ain't no crime, and it
certainly has helped a lot to make presidents. [*To* FREDDIE.]
Will you quit that! How many times must I tell you not
to push your fingers through tears in your clothes! Goodness sakes! You'll drive me crazy yet.

FATHER

[*Refilling his pipe and lighting it again, speaking once
more in the same thoughtful, quiet tone.*] Say, Maw . . .

MOTHER

[*Talking on, unheeding.*] Now, get into your nightie! Come
on; I can't wait all night.

FATHER

Say, Maw!

MOTHER

[*Tired.*] Well, what is it?

FATHER

[*Smoking, and speaking mildly and slowly.*] Say, Maw, I've
been thinkin'.

MOTHER
[*Without interest.*] You have?

FATHER
Yep! I've been thinkin'.

[*A pause, as the* FATHER *smokes.*]

MOTHER
Well, what've you been thinking?

FATHER
Maw, I've been thinkin'. I've been figgerin' out a scheme,
Maw—great scheme.

MOTHER
What about?

FATHER
Yep, I got a scheme, Maw; got it all figgered out how to
get rich—quick—right to the top.

MOTHER
[*Without interest.*] Oh!

[*A pause.*]

FATHER
Want to hear my scheme, Maw? [*He begins to show excitement, and rises.*]

MOTHER
[*To* FREDDIE.] Say your prayers, now, Freddie. Come on;
hurry up!

[FREDDIE *kneels at the right side of the bed. The* FATHER
subsides into his chair and begins smoking again. The
MOTHER *sits on the bed, without much interest in the
prayer.*]

"Now I lay me . . ."

FREDDIE

"Now I lay me—down to sleep I—pray the Lor' . . . [*He stops.*]

MOTHER

[*Her mind not on it.*] My soul to take . . .

FREDDIE

[*Roused.*] You got that wrong, Mama. I pray the Lor'— my soul to keep. [*Then fast.*] If I should die before I wake —pray the Lor' my soul t' take. [*He slows up.*] Go' bless Mamma. Go' bless Papa—make me a goo' boy—an' successful an' famous—n'amen!"

MOTHER

Hurry into bed now and shut your eyes and go right to sleep!

[FREDDIE *stumbles sleepily to his small bed, and the* MOTHER *puts him in and covers him.*]

FATHER

Say, Maw . . .

MOTHER

What? [*She crosses down to the bed again and sits, braiding her hair.*]

FATHER

Want to hear my scheme?

MOTHER

Tell me, if you feel like it.

FATHER

[*Taking the pipe from his mouth and pointing it at her.*] Maw, what gets the flies?

MOTHER

[*Turning slightly toward him, and speaking over her shoulder.*] The *flies? What* flies?

FATHER

The *flies—any* flies—*you* know.

MOTHER

[*Facing down right again, uninterested.*] I don't know.
What gets them?

FATHER

[*Impressively.*] Not vinegar—m'lasses!

MOTHER

Well, I suppose it does.

[*Pause.*]

FATHER

Well, Maw, that's my scheme!

MOTHER

What do you mean is your scheme?

FATHER

M'lasses!—*get* 'em with m'lasses!

[*The train whistle is heard close now, as the train pulls
in and comes to a stop apparently just outside an exit
door mid-way down the right aisle of the theater.* JOE
*gets up, and bangs the screen door several times, but it
can hardly be heard above the noise of the train, dis-
charging its passengers at the station.*]

MOTHER

Get *who* with molasses?

FATHER

Cust'mers. [*With growing excitement.*] Now, look here,
Maw. It's m'lasses gets the flies; the flies got the cash.
Now, just as soon as we start spreadin' m'lasses round here,
the flies'll come. We'll get the cash. We gotta quit bein'
sour on the world. We gotta smile—smile—all the time.
We gotta spread the m'lasses. You gotta be m'lasses; I

gotta be m'lasses. Smile and joke; it's smiles makes the world go 'round, Maw—smiles 'n' m'lasses. There ain't a one big business in the country t'day that ain't built up outta smiles—m'lasses—jokes. That's the way to get 'em! We haven't been cheerful enough, Maw; that's why we ain't got along. That's it!

[*During this conversation, a few scattered commuters appear at the aisle door, with brief-cases and newspapers, walk toward the stage, up a side ramp, and are seen to disappear around the window of the shop, and off left, along the street. The train pulls out. The* FATHER *continues.*]

Quicker'n you can say, "Scat," Maw, we'll have this place filled day 'n' night with all the people in the town.

[JOE *walks heavily, whistles a little, clears his throat to attract attention, then deliberately whistles,* "Hot Time in the Old Town Tonight." *He does not stop until after the following speech of the* FATHER.]

Quicker'n you can say, "Scat!" Smile at 'em. Entertain 'em. Make 'em feel at home; that's what they want—'specially the young folks. Bright conversation—m'lasses . . . Two years betcha we'll put on 'naddition here 'n' have the biggest eatin' joint in the state. They'll come here fr'm all over—cheerful—happy—glad. Gotta smile 'n' entertain, Maw; that's it—m'lasses. We gotta be ambitious; gotta have more the American spirit. We gotta get the young folks; the young folks, Maw, that's it—comin' down Turner's Pike to the Junction here from Bidwell every night. They want some place to go. That's what they walk down here for, the young fellows 'n' their girls. I tell you, they want some place to go. All we gotta do is to smile at 'em 'n' entertain 'em 'n' we'll get rich quicker'n that. [*He snaps his fingers.*] M'lasses, Maw, that's it!

M O T H E R

Well, maybe, I don't know. We'll see. But somebody's come in.

F A T H E R

[*Still pacing and excited.*] That's it—some place to go—entertainment. I wouldn't take a million dollars for the place now. Gotta be cheerful. They want some place to go.

[*By now,* JOE *has discovered a small bell on the counter, and bangs on it.*]

M O T H E R

Somebody's come in, I tell you. One of the train gang, likely. Better go and see!

F A T H E R

Huh! [*He is still lost in his dream.*]

M O T H E R

Oh, come out of it! Somebody's come in, I'm saying! See what they want!

F A T H E R

Oh! [*He goes abstractedly toward the door between the rooms, puffing his pipe. He stops abruptly, turns, goes back through the doorway, and excitedly runs down to the side of the bed, leaning over it, speaking in a loud whisper.*] It's Joe Kane! The doctor's son!

M O T H E R

Well, what of it?

F A T H E R

[*Almost dancing.*] Don'cha see? [*As he talks, he blunders about hastily, stripping off the dirty apron, which he drops on the floor, bringing a clean apron from behind the curtain, and tying it around his waist, tidying his unruly hair and mustache with a small pocket comb, standing in front*

*of the mirror as he does so, and then bringing a clean towel
from behind the curtain, and hanging it over his arm.*]

Joe Kane, richest young blood in town—goin' to get him!
Goin' to get him, Maw. Goin' to entertain him—see—
smile at him—see—entertain him. He'll come back with
all the swell people of Bidwell. Gosh, Maw, he's our start;
he come right out of Heaven to us, he did, Maw. You
wait; you see—I'll get him laughin'. M'lasses, Maw—you
see . . .

MOTHER

Better take my advice and let this new fangled entertainment alone. You ain't no showman. [*She lies wearily on
the bed, and pulls the covers over herself.*]

FATHER

All you gotta do, Maw, is mind your own business. I ain't
no showman, maybe, but I got a trick or two in me you
don't know nothin' about. 'N' I ain't goin' to run a one-
horse restaurant all my life, either. It's the first time that
fellow's been in here, 'n' after I get through with him, he's
goin' to come back 'n' bring a crowd with him. You wait
'n' see, Maw! It's my own scheme, 'n' I know how to make
it work. It's our big start, Maw.

[*He enters the restaurant, where* JOE *has, by this time,
resumed his seat at the table, and is reading his paper,
his back toward* FATHER.]

MOTHER

[*As the light dims on the bedroom side.*] Well, maybe. I've
got my doubt.

[FATHER *makes a patent effort to smile, and give forth
cheerfulness. He even rubs his hands together. He
pauses several times between the door he has left and
the back of* JOE'S *chair, which apparently is his destination. It is certain that the nearer he gets to* JOE, *and*

the longer the time that passes, the quicker go his assurance and smile. After a long pause, directly behind JOE'S *chair, the* FATHER *raises his hand high, as if to give his guest a cordial slap on the back, and keeps it aloft a moment, in doubt. It finally comes down, with too great force, for the impact unbalances* JOE. JOE *drops his paper and falls forward to the floor in one direction, the chair in another, the* FATHER'S *pipe in a third.* JOE *picks himself up, and* JOE *and* FATHER *stand absolutely still, staring at each other for several moments, their faces expressing only blank amazement. The* FATHER *finally takes a step forward.* JOE *is undecided whether to run for the door or adopt an attitude of defense. He partially does the latter, and again for a moment the two face each other, amazed and motionless.*]

FATHER

Gee, Joe . . . Gee, Mr. Kane—mistake—didn't mean . . . Hurt? Get hurt at all? Fool I am; that's what I am. Here—what the'll anyway? Here, lemme brush you off.

[*He has picked up the chair, the paper, and his own pipe, and handed them all to* JOE, *who takes them in a dazed way, brushing himself off and rubbing himself. The* MOTHER *has jumped out of bed, at the crash, and is listening through the thin partition. She shakes her head, and goes back to sit dejectedly on the side of the bed.*]

Gee—didn't mean it—nothin' like that, you know. You know I was just tryin' to give you a little slap on the back, you know—friendly—you know, hail fellow, well met, eh? Friendly like, you know. How you feel now?

JOE

Oh, I'm okay. That's all right; forget about it. That's all right.

F A T H E R

Gee—we aim to please. Lemme get ya glass of water.

J O E

I'm all right.

[FATHER *gets a glass of water from behind the counter, and brings it down to* JOE.]

F A T H E R

[*Trying to smile again.*] Sit down—huh—have a cup of coffee, huh? 'N' a cigar? Where's my pipe—what hell I do with my pipe?

[FATHER *looks through his pockets, and on the counter; then both* FATHER *and* JOE *look on the floor and under the table.*]

J O E

[*Who, unknowingly, has been holding the pipe in his hand.*] Oh, here it is! Guess I must have picked it up when —when . . .

F A T H E R

[*Laughing.*] Much obliged. How do you feel? Cup of coffee, huh? 'N' a cigar, huh? On me—on the house.

[FATHER *brings the cigar from the case, and lights it for* JOE; *then he goes behind the counter to get the coffee, while* JOE *returns to his chair.* JOE *is very skeptical about the cigar.*]

Good cup hot coffee fixes anybody up. Coffee's one of our good specialties here. How you fixed now? All right?

J O E

Thanks. Much obliged. I'm all right. Father's been out of town; coming home tonight, and the darn train's late. So thought I'd come in and have a cup of coffee instead of going back uptown. Don't mind, do you?

FATHER

[*Bringing the cup of coffee down to* JOE, *and shoving the sugar bowl over where it is handy.*] That's right. That's right—just what we're here for—just what . . . Want this to be a real place of entertainment for everybody. Make yourself at home! Drop in any time! We're running a real first-class day 'n' night place here.

[*A pause.* JOE *takes a swallow of coffee, making a face.* FATHER *leans against the counter and puffs his pipe. He has run out of ideas and is obviously uncomfortable, seeking for more.*]

JOE

How's business?

FATHER

Fine—fine. [*Smiling hard.*] Gettin' better right along. [*He goes to the counter, and pours himself a cup of coffee.*] Yep, got a first-class breezy place here. [*Gradually loses enthusiasm.*] Always entertaining. 'N' they keep comin' right along. Yep—yep—fine!

JOE

[*Coughing slightly over his cigar.*] About how many do you feed here in a day?

FATHER

[*Obviously uncomfortable.*] Oh, quite a few—quite a few. Not so many at breakfast as at dinner—but quite a few. Yep—yep—take breakfast, dinner, and supper, together, 'n' the night parties, 'n' we're kept pretty busy, y'know. Yep, people like it—like the entertainment here, y'know.

JOE

Uh-huh. But where do they come from? There don't seem to be many . . .

FATHER

Oh, all over.

[*He carries his cup of coffee down to the table where* JOE *sits, and sits beside him. It is evident that* JOE *is not used to cigars, and is having more and more trouble with this one.*]

Every morning 'n' night the buses come down to the station, y'know, along Turner's Pike from the hotel up in Bidwell; 'n' travelin' men are always waitin' aroun' to take trains; 'n' some of the fellows come over from the cider mill 'n' pickle factory; 'n' when the local freight crew finishes their switchin' in Pickleville they always come in for a meal. Oh, yes, lots of people—fine people, too. Well, y'see, we try to entertain 'em good whenever they come in. Good feed—good entertainment—that's the secret of our success—just like now, y'see.

[JOE *gulps a little, and reaches for the glass of water. But the* FATHER *does not notice his move, and being thoroughly interested in his own story, he picks up the glass first, and drinks from it.* JOE *looks at him in consternation, but the* FATHER *continues.*]

You come in—you get good eats 'n' entertainment; next thing y'know when you want a place to go, you come back —ain't that it?

J O E

[*Flatly.*] Yes, I guess so. But how d'you entertain them?

FATHER

[*Uncomfortably.*] Huh? Why . . .

J O E

What do you do to entertain them?

FATHER

[*Weakly.*] Well, what do you call . . . Yeah, yeah, entertain—what do you think I'm . . . Have another cup of coffee, huh?

[JOE *puts up his hand negatively, and the* FATHER *puffs desperately at his pipe.*]

No? Suit yourself; suit yourself. Say, you know I wa'n't always in the restaurant business. Oh, no—nope. I was in the chicken business, 'for, y'know, 'for I made a success of this place, y'know. Yep, I was a pretty big chicken man. Yeah, a big place, ten acres—kinda stony but then it was all right. Had a place just outside Bidwell, y'know, eight miles out on Grigg's Road. Y'know it?

JOE
No.

[*He is covertly reading the paper again.* FATHER *gets up for another cup of coffee for himself, and this time brings the porcelain coffee pot to the table and sets it down between them.*]

FATHER
Yep, quite a place. The missus put me up to do it, y'know. Fine woman, the missus—smart woman—y'betcha. I didn't really get my start in life till I got t'know her. That was when I was—let's see—oh, well, 'bout—oh, thirty, yeah—'bout thirty-four years. Usta work for Tom Butterworth, out'n the Bidwell Road, y'know. Know Tom?

JOE
Oh, I just know who he is.

FATHER
Fine fellow, Tom. Yes—fine fellow, all right. [*He smokes.*] Gave me pretty good pay, Tom did. Had my own jalopy. Usta drive into town ev'ry Saturday night. Gang was always at Ben Head's saloon, y'know. Bunch of fine fellas—yes, they was. I'd take a glass of beer or so, 'n' ev'ry once 'n' a while I'd get tanked, y'know. Now, I didn't want to; didn't like it—always made me pretty sick. But then, y'know how it is: fellas get singin' 'n' thumpin' their

glasses on the bar 'n' want you to have one on 'em. Oh, y'know how it is; y'can't be a stiff; y'gotta do what the gang does, y'know. Well, then about ten, usta drive home feelin' pretty good, 'n' singin' a little now 'n' then, 'n' roll into bed. Great days, them were—yep, great days; that's no joke. [*He sighs in enjoyable memory, then smokes, lost in thought. He suddenly remembers he must entertain. He pours some coffee into both cups, from the pot.*] Yep— yep. Good coffee! 'N' then the missus came along. She was a school teacher, y'know; mighty smart woman, too— yep—smart woman. She was the makin' of me, y'know— yep. Gotta give her credit for that. She made me what I am today; told me I was too good a man for farm-hand. Yep, she's bright, all right. I was just like the other fellas till she came along—kinda shifters, y'know. Got gray eyes, y'know; 'n' they're always smart women. Got me off Tom's farm 'n' made me sell the jalopy 'n' go into business for myself. Chicken farm, y'know; went big, too. I'm a pretty good chicken man, if I do say it. Yep, I've handled thousands of eggs. No one knows the game better'n I do, if I do say it. Lotsa money in it, too. Y'see, it's a easy game when you get on to it. All y'gotta have is a bunch of chickens, 'n' the chickens lay eggs, 'n' you hatch those eggs 'n' then raise those chicks, 'n' those chicks lay more eggs 'n' y'raise up the chickens from those eggs—see, that's all. It just sorta keeps on goin' by itself like a wheel, y'know. Pile of money in it.

JOE

Yes, guess there is. But there's a lot 'round here who lost a pile of money chicken farming, too.

FATHER

Dam' right. Gotta know the game; that's the whole thing. Gotta know it from the egg up to the layer. Helluva game if y'don't know it.

JOE
But you know it!

FATHER
Oh, yes. Y'see, nothin' can have so much happen to it in so many different places as a chicken can. They come outa their shells lookin' all fluffy 'n' nice, like Easter cards, y'know. Then you get thinkin' you're goin' to have a bunch of hens in a few months. 'N' then they lose all their feathers 'n' run around naked 'n' eat more corn 'n' meal than you can raise in the state of Ohio. Then they get diseases like pip 'n' cholera, 'n' begin blinkin' their eyes up at the sun, 'n' then turn up their toes 'n' die. 'N' if that don't kill 'em, the mice 'n' rats do. 'N' if you do get a hen or a rooster or two that skins through, they get squashed under wheels. 'N' if there's any come through, you gotta hand over all the money you got left for vermin powders, Wilmer's Wonder Cholera Cure, or Prof. Bedlow's egg producer, or something else the odds in the chicken. And then there's coccidiosis!

JOE
[*Alerted by this bit of information.*] There's what?

FATHER
Coccidiosis. That's a terrible disease. Y'don't even know they've got it till they die by the hundreds. *Nobody* knows what to do for coccidiosis.

JOE
But you know what to do for coccidiosis!

FATHER
Yep—yep—terrible disease! Why, even the *County Agents* don't know what to do for coccidiosis!

JOE
No?

FATHER

No. Terrible disease! . . . 'N' the trouble is the chickens are always raisin' your hopes. They look so bright 'n' lively, 'n' then you find out they're just stupid—just like people. Y'don't know whether people is better'n chickens or chickens is better'n people, y'know. Say, d'y' ever read any the literature on chickens?

JOE

What?

FATHER

Say! D'y' ever read any the stuff they print about how to make a million dollars on a sixteen-dollar chicken farm?

JOE

No.

FATHER

Well, don't do it. Don't you believe any the lies those chicken 'n' incubator fellas print; let 'em alone.

JOE

But I thought you made money at it.

FATHER

Who? Me? Well, I should say so; sure I did—sure! I made a pretty good pile. Yep, I was one of the few who got along all right. But, y'see, the missus wanted—oh, y'know—y'know . . . She wanted to get along better, y'know, 'n' there was the boy, y'know. The missus wanted to do it, y'know. Got thinkin' of the boy 'n' a better place to raise him. So we got our stuff together 'n' borrowed a truck from Al Grigg—know Al?

JOE

Uh-huh.

FATHER

Fine fella, Al. Yep, none better. Gave us his truck, 'n' we

piled our stuff on it—beds 'n' tables 'n' boxes 'n' chairs 'n' dishes 'n' crate live chickens 'n' the baby carriage. The missus 'n' the boy walked 'n' picked up what fell off—yep, quite a load for a small truck. We packed up 'n' came over here 'n' put our capital in this place, y'know. 'N' it's goin' good, too. Yep, all right.

[*A pause.* JOE *reads,* FATHER *smokes and smiles.*]

Say, guess what?

JOE
What?

FATHER
How'd you like to have seven legs and two heads?

JOE
[*Slightly startled.*] I don't know.

FATHER
How'd you like to see someone with seven legs and two heads?

JOE
[*Uncomfortably.*] All right, I guess.

FATHER
Wait! Get ready for the surprise of your life!

[FATHER *goes to a shelf back of the counter and brings out a case containing several bottles. He exhibits each one in turn to* JOE, *who becomes more and more uncomfortable and sick.*]

Y'see, on a chicken farm, when y'get thousands chickens comin' outa eggs, lots s'prisin' things happen. About once every thousand eggs, then somethin' wonderful happens: a freak comes out. Got one right here! [*He shows one bottle to* JOE, *who turns away.*] Hellavit is they don't live; that's what got me sore a' the chicken business. If I coulda raised one of these freaks into a rooster or a hen, I could taken 'em round to county fairs 'n' gotten rich. Anybody'd paid twenty-five cents admission to see things like that, wouldn't they? But I got 'em all preserved here, all right; got 'em in alc-hol just as they was. Now, here's where you're going to see somethin'! Ain't a collection like this any place in the world. Look at that! Huh? Here's another: four wings. D'y' ever see anything like that?

[JOE *begins to feel painfully ill.*]

'N' look at that—born that way 'n' lived ten days. 'N' here she is, one of the greatest wonders of the world: seven legs 'n' two heads! Ain't that a beaut?

[JOE *rises abruptly and starts toward the outer door.*]

What's matter? Where you go?

JOE
Guess I'd better go out and see about the train. Feel a little sick, anyway.

FATHER
[*Crossing to him, and taking him by the arm.*] Oh, what the . . . ? Mustn't mind a little thing like that? These are wonders; wouldn't take a thousand dollars for 'em. Nope, ain't every restaurant can show you things like that.

[FATHER *leads* JOE *back to the table.* JOE *is slightly angry, and beginning to be desperate.*]

Missus wants me to throw them out, but I won't do it. Too valuable, 'n' everybody likes to look at strange 'n' wonderful things like that.

JOE
You may be right. [*He sits sulkily at the table again.*]

FATHER
Just wanted you to feel at home. Make it a point here to

entertain all our guests. Ain't no more cheerful restaurant west of New York! [*He takes* JOE's *cup, and crosses to the counter again.*] C'mon, have another cup of coffee 'n' a cigar—my treat! Always want to please. [*He hurries back with a cigar, which he lights for* JOE.] Well—well, now . . . Say, you have heard of Christopher Columbus, haven't you? [*He goes behind the counter, pours from a milk bottle into* JOE's *cup, brings the cup back to the table, and refills it from the coffee pot.*]

JOE

Sure. [*He has ceased to try to be polite.*]

FATHER

Well, what d'you think of a man like that, now? What do you think of him?

JOE

He's all right, isn't he?

FATHER

All right? Is that what you say? Why, that man's the biggest joke, the biggest cheat ever lived. Nothin' but a liar 'n' a cheat. Get so mad when I hear 'bout him I feel like burnin' all the school houses down. Low-doun cheat! 'N' yet they teach the kids all 'bout him in the schools, give him monuments—great man! Gee—said he could make an egg stand on end, 'n' then he went 'n' broke the end of the egg. 'N' that's the kind of man we had discover America for us. Cheat 'n' liar, wasn't he?

JOE

Guess so.

FATHER

But *I* c'n make an egg stand on end, 'n' I don't cheat; but *I* don't get any monuments, do I? I don't get in no history books. It ain't fair, I tell you. [*He takes an egg from the plate on the counter.*] Look, here' a egg; now watch! I'll roll it in my hands—look—see? [*He paces excitedly back and forth.*] I know a lot about eggs. No one knows more about 'em than I do. Now look—watch: I'm goin' to show you how I can do what Columbus, the cheater, couldn't! See, I'll make a egg stand on its end, without breaking its shell. Wonderful trick! Gotta know all about eggs 'n' gravity to do it. See, I got a lotta 'lectricity in my hands, 'n' the 'lectricity works on the laws of gravity in the eggs so that the center of the laws of gravity in the egg changes so it'll stand on end. Now look, it's ready; look— wait—see! Wait a minute.

[FATHER *stands his egg on the counter several times, and each time it rolls over on its side. When he does succeed, he looks up to find that* JOE *is reading the paper.*]

Look! Hey—the egg—the egg—Columbus—hey—Kane —Mr. Kane!

[JOE *looks up, but not until the egg has fallen on its side again. He laughs a little, and goes back to his paper. The* FATHER *is now greatly excited. He smokes hard, and runs his fingers through his hair. Through the next speech, the train whistle is heard twice, first faintly, and then close.*]

But here! Wait a minute, here's something I'll do for you. [*He goes behind the counter and picks up a pan containing vinegar and an egg.*] Here's a trick! Here's something worth while. You've never saw this done before. You see it once, you want to see it again, and you'll bring the whole town with you. Can't get any better entertainment any place than what you can here. What we're here for: make our customers cheerful. Bran' new trick! See— vinegar in this pan! I'm treatin' this egg in the vinegar— see? Then I'll make it go down the neck of the bottle. After it goes through the neck, it will look like a egg again, and get hard. Then I'm goin' to make you a present of the egg in the bottle. Yep, that's what we're here for: to entertain. No charge. You c'n take it along whenever you go. Everybody'll ask you how you got the egg in the bottle. Keep mum 'n' don't tell 'em; keep 'em guessin'. Gee, you can have a lot of fun with this trick.

[*Through this speech,* FATHER *grins and smiles at* JOE, *who appears to consider the* FATHER *a harmless lunatic, and reads his paper. The* FATHER *takes the egg from the vinegar with a spoon, and tries to force it into the neck of a bottle. He mutters as he does so, and constantly glances at* JOE *to see if he is interested.* JOE'S *lack of interest enrages him. As the egg seems about to enter the bottle, the train whistle is heard again, loud, as the train pulls into the station and stops.* JOE *gets up and moves toward the door, then turns to look at the anxious, sputtering* FATHER, *just at the moment when the latter breaks the egg, which spurts over him.*]

JOE

[*At the door.*] Ha! Ha! Great trick!

[*The* FATHER *utters a strange cry of frustration and anger. He seizes another egg, runs from the counter, and hurls it at* JOE, *who escapes through the door just in time. The egg breaks over the screen door. The* FATHER *rushes back for another egg, inarticulate in his rage. He turns to find there is no one to throw it at; and a change comes over him. His arm drops. He gives one despairing look about him. He closes the front door without locking it, and turns down the oil lamp. He becomes aware that the egg is still in his hand. He looks at it and places it on the table. As he does so, the tension under which he has been acting breaks, and with deep but quiet sobs, he throws himself into the chair, his head in his hands. The* MOTHER, *who has been listening*

at the wall during the end of the scene, comes into the
restaurant without speaking. She puts her arms tenderly about the FATHER'S shoulders. Now the commuters are coming from the train and passing by the
restaurant, as before. The whistle blows loudly, as the
train picks up speed and chugs away. The people pass
the restaurant in a gay mood. JOE and his father appear.
JOE seems to be talking and gesturing about the crazy
man and the eggs. They both look with curiosity and
amusement into the restaurant as they pass. They do
not stop, and the laughter from outside mingles with
the sobbing within.]

THE FEAST
OF ORTOLANS

A Drama of the French Revolution

By Maxwell Anderson

From 20 One-Act Classics *edited by Margaret Mayorga. Copyright 1937 by Maxwell Anderson. Reprinted by permission of Chilton Books, Philadelphia and New York.* Amateurs may produce this play without payment of royalty provided admission is not charged.

CAST

The Duke of Pompignan, the host.

La Harpe, the prophet of the revolution.

André Chénier, the poet.

Théroigne, the woman he loves.

Phillippe d'Orléans, heir to the throne of France.

Lafayette, hero of the American Revolution.

Beaumarchais, the playwright.

Duchess du Gramont, a lady of fashion.

Mlle. Vergniaud de Sombreuil, a belle.

General Custine, in the service of the king.

Lieutenant Custine, his son.

Desmoulins, the editor.

Champfort, a guest.

Condorcet, a guest.

Bailly, a guest.

Malesherbes, a guest.

Roucher, a guest.

The Chef.

Two Servants.

In the year 1789 a group of writers, artists, intellectuals, and, mingled with them, a scattering of nobles, are seated around the great dinner table in the residence of the Duke of Pompignan, not more than twenty miles from Paris. The occasion is the Feast of Ortolans,* a ceremony observed once a year by the Pompignan family during the reigns of the last three kings who bore the name of Louis. It is a ceremony which has grown out of the family custom of serving a special and remarkable dish of ortolans once in the year to the most intimate as well as the most distinguished friends of the family. This gallant and famous dish has not yet been brought in, but the guests have already whetted their appetites on hors d'oeuvres and the first wine.

POMPIGNAN
And things shall be thus in that great day, my masters: there shall be five quarters in the year, seven feet to the ell, ten days to the week, and all days paydays; the ounce shall be equal to the pound in every scale, the half-crown equal to the crown, the rod to the mile, the woman to the man. The king shall be Marie Antoinette, and Marie Antoinette shall be the king——

[*There is a burst of laughter from the table.*]

BEAUMARCHAIS
And more——

CHAMPFORT
More and no miracle——

* Ortolan. *A bird netted and fattened for a table delicacy.*—Webster.

[*More laughter with an undertone of conversation.*]

DUCHESS DU GRAMONT
Gentlemen, gentlemen, not all together, please. You
drown each other with wit, and we poor women are left
wondering what was said——

CONDORCET
Forgive us, Madame la Duchesse, but for this once you
were not supposed to hear——

THE DUCHESS
Not to hear—and why?

CONDORCET
To spare your cheeks, Madame, lest those who blush easily
should never blush again without art, and lest those who
blush by technique, as say, by holding the breath, or by
pressure on the jugular, should do themselves a mischief.

MLLE. DE SOMBREUIL
But I've heard nothing really scandalous for years. I'm
quite out of practice with my blushing!

POMPIGNAN
At the feast of ortolons, my dear, we expect the men to be
ribald and the women to be discreet, but when our ribaldry
outruns your discretion, as it will, at times, we cover the
words with untimely laughter.

THE DUCHESS
Ah, but women are to be equal with men in that new day,
are they not, Vergniaud?

MLLE. DE SOMBREUIL
Equal or above them!

POMPIGNAN
But not equal in wickedness, surely?

THE DUCHESS

Oh, above them in wickedness, as indeed they are now. All the Encyclopedists say so. Women have a natural genius for wickedness, whereas men are naturally moral, even docile, clinging to the Decalogue as a drowning man clings to his chicken coop——

MLLE. DE SOMBREUIL

Yes; man, man—a creature of good habits, broken to harness by the mere offer of sweetmeats——

PHILIPPE D'ORLÉANS

Not all of us——

MLLE. DE SOMBREUIL

Not the soldiers, no—but all the rest——

PHILIPPE

And not the artists——

MLLE. DE SOMBREUIL

I grant you—not the soldiers or artists—

CHAMPFORT

But here tonight we are all soldiers or artists——

MLLE. DE SOMBREUIL

And when have we married any of you here tonight? No, no, we women know a manageable man by his occupation. A solid Breton with a fur business in the Rue Vaugirard, a bald and aging banker with an estate at Versailles and a house in the city, these we lead with a show of sugarplums to the altar of Saint Eustache——

POMPIGNAN

But all this too will vanish in the new era, in the light of freedom and reason, Mademoiselle. In that glorious dawn there shall be no marrying or giving in marriage, and man will doff his gyves.

THE DUCHESS

Then I begin to have my doubts of the wisdom of revolution altogether.

LA HARPE

Would you have things go on as they are, dear lady?

MALESHERBES

They cannot go on as they are. As time goes on, men become wiser, and they must apply their wisdom to the state.

MLLE. DE SOMBREUIL

But not to the state of marriage!

POMPIGNAN

To marriage, to religion, to law—there is even talk of reforming the calendar—and the multiplication table is to be rearranged so that what a man has in his pocket will always equal what he needs to live on.

THÉROIGNE

[*Aside to* CHÉNIER *while another conversation proceeds in an undertone.*] Who is the pale, grave gentleman who wears the order of the Golden Fleece and takes no part in the conversation?

CHÉNIER

[*Aside.*] Are you caught by the noble profile, Théroigne? Never mind, he's no ladies' man, and you may abandon the idea at once. He is the Marquis de Lafayette, hero of the revolution in the new world, friend of Washington, a saint in private life, much in love with his wife and beyond temptation.

THÉROIGNE

[*Aside.*] And the patrician with the burnished bronze face, to the left, his breast covered with orders?

CHÉNIER

You look high, my darling. You have an instinct for impossibilities. He is only Philippe d'Orléans, prince of the blood and heir to the throne of France.

THÉROIGNE

Ah.

CHÉNIER

No more?

THÉROIGNE

Yes—the tall, imperious-looking one, who could be more witty than any if he tried?

CHÉNIER

To the right of the prince?

THÉROIGNE

Yes.

CHÉNIER

Beaumarchais. The playwright, the author of "Figaro." The fellow who made a fortune on paper out of the American Revolution, but has not yet been paid, and who hopes to make a fortune out of the revolution here.

THÉROIGNE

He's very handsome.

CHÉNIER

Oh, and a devil with the women. Come, darling, are we unhappy already that you begin to cast about for another?

THÉROIGNE

You'll tire of me, you know.

CHÉNIER

You anticipate.

THÉROIGNE

And when you have tired of me, surely it would be better to go up and not down.

CHÉNIER

Too candid to be flattering.

THÉROIGNE

Dear André, I love you very much, and I shall not quit you. You will quit me—and when that happens it would be as well to have a foothold——

CHÉNIER

A step higher.

THÉROIGNE

If possible a thought higher——

CHÉNIER

There, I understand you. And I've watched many a pretty woman climb to a pretty career on the shoulders of successive lovers. But never before has one confided her plans to me in advance. This too is revolutionary.

THÉROIGNE

The candor, perhaps, not the method.

CHÉNIER

The method is as old as the world. And for women perhaps the best.

[*They continue conversing in undertones during next speeches.*]

GEN. CUSTINE

[*Loudly.*] But look at the conditions, Monsieur Condorcet, look at the conditions! It may all come out well as you say, but the disorders are becoming insupportable! There was a mob stopping carriages on the Pont Neuf this evening, merely for the fun of making well-to-do folk cry

"Down with the King!" They were harmless enough, and quite good-humored, but they insisted on "Down with the King!"

BEAUMARCHAIS
And did you cry "Down with the King!" General?

GEN. CUSTINE
I did, indeed; otherwise they would have turned the horses quite around and sent me back whence I came.

THE DUCHESS
But that's marvelous!

GEN. CUSTINE
Isn't it? And my friend Revillon, the manufacturer, was actually besieged in his house for having said a workman could live on fifteen sous a day.

POMPIGNAN
Besieged? When?

GEN. CUSTINE
Yesterday. He was a fool to say it, no doubt, but a man should be allowed to speak his mind. And a man's house and carriage should be his own. There should be no interference with private property.

POMPIGNAN
The police should deal with such matters.

GEN. CUSTINE
I have no expectation of real violence, of course. We are a gentle, submissive, peaceful folk, we people of France. But at present there's no discipline. The government allows the workmen to do as they please.

LAFAYETTE
To be quite frank, gentlemen, the lower classes are badly

paid and heavily taxed. Much of the present disorder arises from your refusal to accept a levy on your estates.

POMPIGNAN
Come now, the nobles of France couldn't support the government half a year if they gave all they had——

BEAUMARCHAIS
It's that confounded national deficit that swallows everything. Year after year we're promised a balanced budget, and year after year the deficit grows—it's up beyond all calculation now, insatiable, and rocketing every day into astronomical figures!

POMPIGNAN
But how's the budget to be balanced when the government's so easy with money on every hand? Money goes out right and left——

LAFAYETTE
Haven't you had your share?

POMPIGNAN
Yes, my share and more. Others were holding out their hands and so I held out my hat. It was filled. I made no difference.

[*Laughter.*]

Service, lads, service! [*He claps his hands.*] There seems to be some delay in changing the plates.

A SERVANT
I'm sorry, Monseigneur.

POMPIGNAN
Pray, why is it? There has been no such hiatus between courses since my ancestors purchased Pompignan.

THE SERVANT
Monseigneur, if I may explain, there has been some

quarrel between the servants and the woodcutters——

POMPIGNAN
And why should that affect us here?

THE SERVANT
Monseigneur, the proper baking of the ortolans requires a white-hot oven which is possible only with wood seasoned under cover. But the woodmen brought green fagots today and would bring no more—and in consequence the chef has quarreled with them——

POMPIGNAN
Never mind; your explanations are tiresome, and my friends are hungry. Let the ortolans be made ready and brought at once.

THE SERVANT
Yes, Monseigneur.

POMPIGNAN
And if there are further quarrels in the kitchen I myself will come to settle them.

THE SERVANT
Yes, Monseigneur. [*He withdraws.*]

POMPIGNAN
This is a maddening contretemps, but let us ignore it, guests and lovers! Your glasses!

[*All lift their glasses.*]

I pledge the revolution, and Philippe d'Orléans! Philippe, heir to the throne and friend of the revolution!

VOICES
The Prince!

[*They drink.*]

PHILIPPE

Let me assume that though I am pledged in jest, dear fellows of the feast, I may answer seriously. There has never reigned in France a juster, nobler, wiser, more lovable king than our Louis. A king who welcomes reform, who gives with both hands, who hears the humblest petition, who suffers with the poor, and understands all classes alike. May the throne never devolve upon me at the expense of his most generous majesty. Yet if it should devolve upon me, things would not go on as they are going. I should convene the States-General. There should be representation in France, and a new way of life. I see about me many who would be my ministers.—Whatever the human mind has conceived in the way of freedom of spirit or of the mind should be inaugurated, even the more experimental. Jean-Jacques Rousseau has given us our religion of liberty, and we should carry it out, even to the recognition of the social contract, the responsibility of the state for the people's welfare. And all, even the woodcutters, should be heard, should air their grievances.

[*There is some applause.*]

THE DUCHESS

Let us hear the woodcutters tonight!

POMPIGNAN

Yes, let us hear them. Let us demonstrate.

PHILIPPE

But not in a spirit of levity, gentlemen. The woodcutters are men of the soil. Their service is an ancient and sacred function. They are men such as we might wish to become, men living with nature and made wise by her laws. They are man himself, innocent, unspoiled by courts, the natural savage, the epitome of Rousseau's gospel, virtue incarnate.

BAILLY

Let us, by all means, have in the woodcutters. And treat them with grave respect.

POMPIGNAN

[*To another* SERVANT.] Sirrah, fetch us a woodcutter.

A SERVANT

Into this presence, Monseigneur?

POMPIGNAN

Into this presence.

THE SERVANT

But, Monseigneur, it may be necessary to wash him——

THE DUCHESS

No, no, unwashed—bring him unwashed!

POMPIGNAN

You hear! An unwashed woodcutter!

THE SERVANT

But, Monseigneur, if he should not wish to come?

POMPIGNAN

Bring him and no more words.

[*The* SERVANT *withdraws.*]

THE DUCHESS

He shall taste the ortolans!

POMPIGNAN

He shall indeed. And so shall we if this kitchen feud has been resolved.

THE DUCHESS

I shall set my cap for this woodcutter.

CHÉNIER

But this is mockery.

POMPIGNAN
No, quite serious.

LAFAYETTE
The lad's right. It is mockery. You've played
with the thought of revolution. While you jest
and the Prince talks of his States-General,
the fires roar underneath, and the old injustice
runs too deep to be cured with summoning
a Parliament. I tell you we now stand
on the threshold of a world in which all men
are equal under law as in the sight
of God Himself. You say it and laugh! I say it,
knowing that when the clothes of rank and power
are shed, and all men naked in the light
of inner godhood, this will not be the world
we know—of privilege, greed, and subterfuge—
but a world of liberty and reason! Nay,
you smile, ready to mock again. Good form
and social usage in this company
require that one be serious in jest
only, and jest in earnest. Purge yourselves
of that spirit, gentlemen, and make what haste
you can toward a citizenship you've never dreamed,
citizenship in a world made just and pure
by the abolition of chains!

POMPIGNAN
Oh, Lafayette,
you shame us all!

BEAUMARCHAIS
No chains, no jails, Marquis?
Men free to do as they please?

LAFAYETTE
If there are criminals
they will be those of us whose privilege

has given us too much power, men in themselves
unspoiled are men of good will. The natural passions
all tend toward justice and mercy.

BEAUMARCHAIS
Oh, that's yourself.
Not all men.

LAFAYETTE
All but the few whose trade it is
to live by their wits on others. Parasites
by birth or training. That's you and me, my friend,
and we must learn from our betters who cut wood
to cook our ortolans.

THE DUCHESS
I have a glimpse
how men might live like angels in a heaven
without distrust.

LAFAYETTE
What is it that makes criminals?
A lack of bread; the winter in clay huts
with little fire; children who have no shoes;
taxes to maintain luxury; we've lived
too long by others' weeping. Say three words
and this is changed—freedom, equality,
brotherhood among men. When men are free
they are men, not animals, reasoning men,
loving their peace, keeping a pride of manhood,
holding no envy.

POMPIGNAN
So said the good Rousseau.

MALESHERBES
Well, let it come. I shall hope.

LAHARPE
Yes, let it come.

CHÉNIER
And may I add a word?

POMPIGNAN
Let the poet speak.
Speak, Chénier.

CHÉNIER
A nation lives and dies;
it runs its course and dies, and what it is
is known in the end by what it leaves behind
for other men to see. Music and song,
painting and poetry, these tell our story
when there's nothing left but records. A free people
sings at its labor and leaves song behind,
loves what it does in handiwork and sets
its dream down in such color and design
as makes all ages wonder. Let us have that
for the people of France, set free.

POMPIGNAN
Let that come too.
I shall hope for it.

THE DUCHESS
And I.

BEAUMARCHAIS
But, Lafayette,
what will our world be like when the revolution
has really come? What are the fruits of it?
How will men live?

LAFAYETTE
You will laugh when I say it,
Beaumarchais. For you finance rebellion
and laugh at it, while you cheer it on, and yet
you build better than you know. There will be no kings,
no capitalists, no nobles, and no armies.

Men will keep their own peace. Loving his land,
each citizen of France in that new day
will farm his frugal acres, grind his corn,
dress his own meat, and bring wood for his fire;
returning, happily wearied, when night falls,
to a simple cottage, where his wife has spun
and woven through the day, and where his children
tend to their lighter tasks. Sitting together
at a plain supper, earned and prepared and grown
in their own fields, each family will make
its little Eden, its own paradise,
without shame or rancor. Those will be the fruits
of our revolution.

BEAUMARCHAIS
Adam and Eve in the garden.

LAFAYETTE
Yes, if you like, Adam and Eve.

BEAUMARCHAIS
This time—no snake, no Cain, no murder?

LA HARPE
Murder enough.

BEAUMARCHAIS
Did you speak, La Harpe?

LA HARPE
I think not—no.

BEAUMARCHAIS
You said "Murder enough."

LA HARPE
Did I say that? Then the rest's better unsaid.

BEAUMARCHAIS
La Harpe, the silent. Shall we not hear from him?

THE DUCHESS
If it's something better unsaid, why then, beyond all
we wish to hear it.

LA HARPE
I speak quite doubtfully,
but it comes to my tongue that you shall live to see
this revolution you hope for. Be content
with that. The rest's not cheerful.

CONDORCET
Say it, man.

BEAUMARCHAIS
Come, out with it.

LA HARPE
Then, I repeat, you shall see it,
this revolution; but do you wish to know
what will come of this revolution, for us all here,
before it's done?

CONDORCET
Do you know?

LA HARPE
I think I know.

BEAUMARCHAIS
A prophet, ho! Bring locusts and wild honey!
We have a prophet!

LA HARPE
I've been troubled lately
with a strange aberration, not a thing
one cares to boast about. On a certain morning,
looking up from my shaving toward the mirror,
I saw how I should die.

BEAUMARCHAIS
A pleasant death?

LA HARPE
No, not pleasant.

CONDORCET
But how, then, how? A prophet
should be more definite.

LA HARPE
Let it suffice
that my aberration troubles me tonight
again, and looking round me at the table
I see your deaths in your faces.

CONDORCET
All men die.
How shall I die? Of too much or too little?
Diet or gout?

LA HARPE
You will die, Monsieur de Condorcet,
on the pavement of a prison cell; you will die
of a poison you carry with you always
to escape the headsman's ax. Yet not a headsman,
no, but a new mechanical contrivance
for cutting off men's heads, a thing designed
to save the axman labor in a time
of numerous executions.

MLLE. DE SOMBREUIL
Ah——

POMPIGNAN
Enough.
This is a stupid jest.

THE DUCHESS
What does he mean?

BEAUMARCHAIS

He's mad. The good La Harpe sat so long silent
he's gone mad like a hermit.

CONDORCET

You could have made
a much better story of it. Let me have
an inkling of romance. Let me die to save
a lady compromised. What was my crime?

LA HARPE

Your crime will be that you once sat at dinner,
with Philippe d'Orléans.

PHILIPPE

He sits with me now.
We are all at dinner together, I believe.
But is that a crime?

LA HARPE

It will be.

PHILIPPE

Against whom, La Harpe?

LA HARPE

Against the revolution.

BEAUMARCHAIS

But our Philippe is a friend of the revolution,
and we are all at dinner with him.

LA HARPE

Yes,
and more than one will die for it.

BEAUMARCHAIS

Come now,
you say it will be a crime to sit at dinner
with d'Orléans. But why he?

LA HARPE
It will be a crime
to be an aristocrat, to have spoken with one,
to give him shelter. It will be a crime
to oppose the government, to write a pamphlet,
to fail in battle, to hold unorthodox
or irregular opinions, to have more money
than any of your neighbors, to wear silk
or keep a carriage, yes, even to be named
or suspect of these things. And for these crimes
the punishment will be death.

CONDORCET
And what has all this
to do with the revolution or the rule
of reason?

LA HARPE
It is exactly as I tell you.
In the name of reason and philosophy;
as part of the program of humanity
and liberty—you will end thus. Oh, but the reign
will veritably be one of reason, for
there will be temples of Reason throughout France;
there will be no other temples at that time
save those to Reason. The people will go mad
in the name of tolerance, and cut men down
in the streets for advising tolerance; to write
or read will be a crime. To speak too well,
to have kept books in a counting house; to buy
too cheap or sell too dear will bring you death
and no appeal.

CHAMPFORT
Dear, dear, I should like to know
How I shall die?

LA HARPE

You, Monsieur de Champfort?
You will cut your veins a dozen times
with a razor in your cell; yet you will linger
and die hard later on.

CHAMPFORT

If we do have
a revolution, I shall have friends in it.
I shall be one of the leaders. I've worked for it
night and day, and though, as you say, I jest,
I jest to some purpose. This will not be forgotten
even in troubled times.

LA HARPE

It will be forgotten.

MALESHERBES

And I? My fortune, please, La Harpe!

BAILLY

And I?

DESMOULINS

And I?

ROUCHER

This way, La Harpe! My fortune, too.

LA HARPE

The revolution will devour its children,
and those who fostered it. You, Malesherbes,
who have done all you can to bring about
a change in the state, you will die on the scaffold.
You, Monsieur Bailly, friend of the people,
proponent of their rights, you on the scaffold;
you, Desmoulins, who have edited and spoken
for the rights of man, you on the scaffold, too.
You, Monsieur Roucher, on the scaffold.

ROUCHER
Heigh-ho;
shall we be inundated by the Turks
and Tartars?

LA HARPE
No, as I said, you will be governed
by philosophy and reason. Those who rule
will be philosophers, and will repeat
all you have said about the bright new world
in which all men are free; in that world's name
you and your children will be put to death,
till the executioners are wearied out
with chopping, and they fling you into rivers,
your arms tied, singly and in groups, and men
are thrown to the mobs for butchery.

POMPIGNAN
You forget
your host, La Harpe! Shall I die by fire or water,
singly or in groups?

LA HARPE
I can tell you nothing.

POMPIGNAN
Why, man, why?

LA HARPE
There's nothing in your face,
nothing beyond tonight.

POMPIGNAN
No future, nothing?

LA HARPE
Nothing beyond tonight. You will die young.

POMPIGNAN
Gad! I shall have to hurry.

BEAUMARCHAIS

Miracles,
nothing but miracles, and am I too
without a future?

LA HARPE

You will escape to England. First,
however, you will hide in a linen closet,
and then in a well. And, not the least miracle,
you will turn Christian.

CHAMPFORT

Now I am relieved.
If we're to die when Beaumarchais turns Christian,
we're all immortal!

THE DUCHESS

As for us poor women,
it's our good fortune not to count for much
in revolutions. They won't trouble about us,
or our ideas.

LA HARPE

And yet this time your sex
will not protect you. No, not age nor beauty,
youth nor desire will succor you. You spoke
of marriage. There will be a new kind of marriage,
the marriage of the revolution. Men and women
bound with their lips together, will be tossed
into the sea, saints, sinners, good and bad,
heroes and courtesans, brigands and nuns,
to swim the Styx in company. This will go on
till people tire of it. You, Madame la Duchesse,
you will be led to the scaffold in a cart,
your arms tied behind you; many will weep
of the ladies who must take that journey with you,
and you will comfort them.

THE DUCHESS
But that's heroic!
You leave me that much, though denying me
absolution and a confessor.

LA HARPE
Oh,
there'll be no absolution or confessors—
only reason and terror. The last victim
who as a royal favor is confessed
will be——

BEAUMARCHAIS
Well—who?

LA HARPE
Will be the King of France.
Nor will Philippe succeed him.

PHILIPPE
I shall be dead?

LA HARPE
Not long after.

PHILIPPE
And when will all this be?

LA HARPE
Within six years.

BEAUMARCHAIS
Ha, ha, ha!

LA HARPE
Chénier will die on the scaffold,
the poet of the revolution. Lafayette
will be driven into exile, having tried
to save the king. Marie Antoinette will die
quite beautifully, on the scaffold.

THÉROIGNE
But me—you don't speak of me!

CHÉNIER
Théroigne! Théroigne!

LA HARPE
You will lead a revolt of women, and the men,
my dear, will cut your head off.

THÉROIGNE AND BEAUMARCHAIS
Ha, ha, ha! Ha, ha!

LA HARPE
The dead will lie in the streets. The dogs will sicken
on the meat of men. You will hear the people cry:
The voice of the people is the voice of gods,
and the gods are athirst! Give them your blood to drink!
Mademoiselle de Sombreuil will pledge
the crowd in blood, drinking the blood of friends
to save her father's life. And this will come
of our reasonable, philosophic emancipation
by revolution.

POMPIGNAN
And the end?

LA HARPE
Why, toward the end
the noise of the tumbrils on the cobblestones
will not slacken all day long, loaded with suspects,
with nobles, all condemned, going their way
to the Place de Grève to die. You will be among them,
the eloquent, the brave, the wise, the fair,
author and artist, prophet—I myself
will be among them. There will not be in France
three men of note left living, whom we've known
in this our time. New leaders will ride in
on the tide of blood. Then one man bloodier

than all the rest, small, and without illusions,
will set himself to master all the world
by preaching our own doctrines, such as freedom
from kings and slavery, till he make himself
an emperor, and all his brothers kings,
and that's the end.

BEAUMARCHAIS
Ha, ha, ha! Are you frightened?
Will you let him scare you with jests? Come,
laugh with me,
give him his due, he is a first-class romancer,
and he's earned a laugh! Ha, ha, ha!

THE WHOLE TABLE
Ha, ha, ha! Ha, ha!

CONDORCET
A real ghost story—and we the ghosts!

THE TABLE
Ha, ha, ha!

[*The laughter mounts, hysterically, into a roar. As it dies
down it merges with confused angry voices outside the
windows.*]

THE VOICES
They shall not have a hostage!
Not one man!
Not one!
Let them eat their ortolans raw!
Raw!
Show us the cook who cooks ortolans!

LAFAYETTE
What can this be?

POMPIGNAN
An altercation in the courtyard! *Peste!* These

carters shall be hung by the thumbs!

THE VOICES
But he wishes only one as a guest!
An honored guest!
Guest, eh?
An honored guest!
He wants a hostage!
We've seen that before!
He shall not have one!
Not one man this time!
Let him come out and take us!
Let him bring his ortolans!
And his guests!

[*A* SERVANT *enters.*]

POMPIGNAN
Silence that rabble in the court! And bring me the ring-
leader!

THE SERVANT
Monseigneur, they will not send a man to you.

POMPIGNAN
Who are they?

THE SERVANT
The woodcutters. They are afraid of punishment and
refuse to send even one, thinking you mean to hold him as
a hostage.

POMPIGNAN
A hostage? Is this a war we wage? I have asked for a
woodcutter. My guests wish to be joined by a woodcutter.
He will be treated kindly. Tell them so.

THE SERVANT
Monseigneur, I have told them. . . .

BEAUMARCHAIS
Ah, the cook himself.

[*The* CHEF *enters from the kitchen, white and trembling.*]

THE DUCHESS
Come to explain.

POMPIGNAN
Perhaps we shall have our ortolans at last—— Why are you here, sirrah? What do you want with us?

THE CHEF
For three generations we have served you, we of my family, at the feast of ortolans. It has been my office alone to prepare this dish—and I had hoped never to fail you—— [*He sits.*]

POMPIGNAN
Why are you here? Why do you sit in my presence?

THE CHEF
But I have failed you. I shall never cover a dish for you again, nor stand at your fire. . . .

POMPIGNAN
Rise! Stand up!

THE CHEF
Yes, Monseigneur. [*He rises.*]

POMPIGNAN
Have you left your senses? Why are you not to cook for me again?

THE CHEF
Because I am dying. [*He falls to the floor.*]

THE DUCHESS
He's ill, Pompignan. There is blood about him on the floor. Do not be angry with him.

POMPIGNAN

Remain here, gentlemen. There has been a quarrel in the kitchen. Remain here while I attend to it. [*To the* SERVANTS.] Take this fellow out. [*He goes to the kitchen.*]

THE DUCHESS

[*To the* SERVANTS.] But lift him gently.

PHILIPPE

Yes.—See, he has a knife wound.

MLLE. DE SOMBREUIL

Oh!

THE DUCHESS

Gently. Gently, please. Tell them to lift him gently.

THE CHEF

And now I shall not serve you any more. [*He is carried out.*]

GEN. CUSTINE

It seems we are to have nothing but disorder this evening. Rioting on the Pont Neuf, feuds in the kitchen, ill omens at the table. . . .

SERVANT

[*Enters and announces.*] Lieutenant Custine, Monseigneur.

GEN. CUSTINE

My son has come. I wondered.

[LIEUTENANT CUSTINE *enters.*]

Why were you late, my son? The place was set for you.

LT. CUSTINE

Forgive my uniform. I had no time to change.—Gentlemen, had any of you intended returning to Paris this evening?

PHILIPPE
Many of us, I think. Perhaps all.

LT. CUSTINE
Then I advise you to take carriage in another direction.
Paris has gone mad. Saint-Antoine is a seething mob.
Many have been killed on both sides. None of the roads is
safe. I came through on horseback with difficulty.

GEN. CUSTINE
You are injured?

LT. CUSTINE
No, no, but I fear I may have injured others. It was necessary to ride them down.—General Lafayette, I have a
message for you. The king asks that you rally a regiment
to form a special guard.

LAFAYETTE
For what purpose?

LT. CUSTINE
To protect the queen and him.

LA HARPE
Ah! It begins to come true! It begins already.

LT. CUSTINE
Something has begun indeed. There has been an attempt
on the Bastille.

LAFAYETTE
By whom?

LT. CUSTINE
By the Paris rabble. I heard that it had fallen, but one
hears many things, and that's impossible.

LAFAYETTE
The Bastille is impregnable.

LT. CUSTINE

Yes. At any rate to a mob armed with scythes and hatchets.
But the city's unsafe.

THE DUCHESS

What must we do?

LT. CUSTINE

Take what roads you like. But not toward Paris.

[*A cry is heard in the distance.*]

Where is our host?

THE DUCHESS

In the kitchen.

LT. CUSTINE

Are you jesting?

THE DUCHESS

No. There was some trouble between the servants and the
woodcutters. He went to settle it.

LT. CUSTINE

Have you let him go alone? The whole country is in flame
and his workmen with the rest. [*He strides to the kitchen
entrance.*]

LAFAYETTE

I'll go with you. [*They go out.*]

GEN. CUSTINE

The lad has never seen service. It may be that he exag-
gerates.

BEAUMARCHAIS

He cannot have seen it with his own eyes. The Bastille has
not fallen, I assure you.

[*There is another cry from the kitchen.*]

PHILIPPE
Where are the servants? They seem to have disappeared.

THE DUCHESS
I feel suddenly oppressed here. As if we were surrounded by invisible things, hemmed in. Someone cried out.

[LAFAYETTE *returns.*]

Where are the servants? We are left unattended here.

LAFAYETTE
They are all gone.

PHILIPPE
And our host?

LAFAYETTE
We found him alone in the kitchen. Dead. A poniard between his shoulders. Face downward in the great dish of ortolans.

LA HARPE
This is the last feast of the ortolans. The gods are athirst. We shall not meet again.

QUARE MEDICINE

By Paul Green

CAST

Old Man Jernigan
Henry Jernigan, his son
Mattie Jernigan, Henry's wife
Doctor Immanuel, a patent-medicine vendor

The scene is the combined sitting-room and bedroom of the JERNIGAN house, with a fireplace to the left, a sewing machine to the right and a table in the center of the room. The floor is carpeted with bright straw matting, and everything bristles with tidy primness. A door is at the center back and one at the left rear. The window at the right center, neatly curtained, shows a streak of somber autumn fields filling up with the blue dusk of a fading winter day. From another part of the house the voice of a woman can be heard shrilly singing "Rescue the perishing, care for the dying." The elder JERNIGAN, walking with a stick, comes carefully in at the rear door shivering with cold and carrying a mug-cup in his hand. Below a mass of white hair his face shines out like a ruddy autumn apple, and his whole person suggests the toughness and durability of a dried hickory root.

Half-way across the room he stops and listens to the singing.

JERNIGAN

[Sharply imitating.] "Rescue the perishing, care for the dying!"

[He moves over to the fire and sets his mug to warm; after which he takes a bottle from the mantel, pours out some medicine in a spoon and swallows it. He sits down and stretches his hands to the blaze with a grunt of satisfaction. In a moment he feels the cup and takes a long drink. The woman's voice calls from off the right.]

V O I C E
Father!

J E R N I G A N
[*Starting.*] Ah-hanh! What is it?

V O I C E
[*Nearer.*] Father—fath—er!

J E R N I G A N
[*Moving towards the door at the left.*] What is it, Mattie?

V O I C E
Supper's 'bout ready. Where's Henry? [*The singing begins again, fading towards the kitchen.*]

J E R N I G A N
[*Calling futilely after her.*] He's feeding up and'll be here in a minnit.

[*He listens awhile and then reseats himself thoughtfully before the fire. Presently there is a heavy scraping of feet on the steps outside and* HENRY JERNIGAN *comes timidly in at the rear. He is a big awkward farmer of thirty or more, hesitating and shy. He takes his seat silently and wearily in a rocking chair, being careful not to touch the whitewashed hearth with his feet. The old man looks at him closely.*]

J E R N I G A N
Tired out, ain't you? Hyuh, try some o' this 'simmon beer, I jest dreaned the barrel.

H E N R Y
[*In a slow, fumbling voice.*] I don't want none o' that, I believe.

J E R N I G A N
Unh-hunh.

[*They both lapse into silence, staring before them. Soon the elder* JERNIGAN *peers through the window at the winter sunset.*]

Gonna be cold, Henry, cold. Robins been flying towards the south all day.

[HENRY *says nothing.*]

You're tireder'n common, ain't you, Henry?

HENRY
Yeh. [*Lifelessly.*] Wore out, wore out.

JERNIGAN
[*Taking his bottle from the mantel.*] Hyuh, take this last dost of Doctor 'Manuel's tonic.

[HENRY *shakes his head.*]

Well, I will then. [*He pours out the last drop and swallows it.*] Doctor said he'd be by today. 'Bout night and he ain't hyuh yit. You better git him to give you something, ye better, Henry, you're looking thin, thin.

HENRY
He ain't no doctor, he's a humbug.

JERNIGAN
Lard help my life!

HENRY
Wonder that mess don't kill you—old branch water and chemicals he's mixed up, I betcha. [*He sighs heavily, listening to the song in the kitchen.*] That old man's crazy with his poetry and talking and medicine!

JERNIGAN
Hunh, not hardly. [*Solemnly.*] 'Tain't body tired what ails ye, Henry, is it? [*After a moment he jerks his thumb in the direction of the song.*] Still singing, Henry. There it is.

HENRY

Yeh, I know.

JERNIGAN

Ah-hah, but folks will marry jest the same. She's worse'n ever, Henry. Good she is, religious good. Cooking and sewing and scrubbing and all fixed up fer tonight. Look over there on the machine at what she's got finished fer them there Hindoos or whatever they are. There's my coat I bought in Dunn five years back at Old Man Ransome Taylor's sale!

HENRY

[*His eyes traveling heavily about the room.*] What's she got on fer tonight?

JERNIGAN

Another one o' them there meetings. Old Mis' Pate and her gang's coming hyuh to sew fer the heathen and them that's starving over in the old world. [*Staring at him intently.*] This religious mess is gonna kill Mattie off ef you don't git up manhood enough to stop it. Sing and talk, sing and talk, Lard, I can't stand it no more.

HENRY

I—I cain't—I ain't gonna put my authority on nobody. She's her own boss.

JERNIGAN

Own boss! She's her own boss and our'n too. Well, ef you're scared of her, all right. They ain't no help fer it. [*He turns towards the fire, patting his foot forlornly on the floor.*] But, Henry, ye ain't getting no fun out'n living, and right now's the time ye ort.—And as fer me—I been wanting to talk—[*Hitching up his chair.*]—to you 'bout this. Why the name o' Old Scratch you don't up and putt down yer foot I cain't see.

[HENRY *says nothing.*]

But ye won't. [*Half to himself.*] He ain't got no backbone, lets everybody run over him. [*He reaches for his cup and drains down the last of his beer in an angry gulp.*] Ye didn't git that from yer mammy ner from me, Henry. [*He mocks the singing in the kitchen.*] "Rescue the perishing——"

HENRY

[*Suddenly standing up.*] I cain't have no row with nobody, not with her nohow, I tell you. [*At the door.*] I got to go part the cow and calf. [*He slams the door behind him and the old man jumps in astonishment.*]

JERNIGAN

Dinged ef he didn't slam the door—hee, hee, hee. Good fer you, Henry, good fer you!

[MATTIE, *a fair faced young woman, comes in from the left, singing and carrying a stone churn in her arms. Despite her housewifely certainty of action, there is an indefinite feminine frailty about her.*]

MATTIE

What's good for Henry?

JERNIGAN

[*Hurrying in confusion to his chair.*] Nothing, Mattie, nothing at all.

[*She looks sharply at him a moment and then sets the churn by the hearth.*]

MATTIE

I'm putting the milk here to turn. I wisht you'd look at it every now and then and stir it with the dasher.

JERNIGAN

All right, Mattie, all right.

MATTIE

And mind, don't you spill none o' that old beer on the hearth.

JERNIGAN
I won't, Mattie, I won't.

MATTIE
What'd Henry go out for?

JERNIGAN
To git the calf away from the cow.

MATTIE
[*The words piling out.*] I bet he didn't wipe his feet when he come in. And did you? [*Staring on the floor and following* HENRY's *trail.*] No, he didn't—just look at the dirt, just look at it. [*She hurries into the room at the left and returns with a broomsedge broom.*] Here, sweep it up, Father. [*She pushes the broom into his hand.*] I've got to go back to my batter. [*She sticks her head out the door at the rear and calls.*] Henry—Hen—ry! Supper!

[*She turns back into the room and old* JERNIGAN *falls to sweeping.*]

Sweep it towards the hearth, towards the hearth, Father, and mind the milk, don't git it full of dust. [*She goes out singing, beginning where she left off.*]—"from sin and the grave——"

JERNIGAN
[*Sweeping.*] Lard, Lard A'mighty, was ever martel man so persecuted! [*Leaning on his broom and musing.*] There he is— [*Nodding his head to the right.*]—pore soul, not at peace in his own household, going about like a man with the mulligrubs, cain't sleep, cain't eat, worried, worried down to the ground. And there she is—[*Nodding to the left.*]—reading the *Christian Herald* and hearing about dirt and disease and famine over in Azhy till she ain't fit to live with. Listen to her, listen to her, will you? What's to become of me, Old Moster only knows. What, to come to this, to this, in my old age and me—[*Thumping on his*

chest.]—yeh, me, old and with a crippled leg from marching in Furginny! [*He wipes his sleeve across his eyes and goes back to sweeping. Presently he stops and begins to muse again.*] Putts me to sweeping, she does, and churning and gitting up the eggs, and following old setting hens around. And she's had me at the wash-tub like an old woman, she has. Damn it! [*His voice sags over the oath.*] I ain't no woman. If Henry ain't got the grit to say something, I have. It's "Father do this, Father do that, Father —Father—Father!" But ding it all, she's a good girl. It's that drot'n old bell-cow of a Bella Pate and her gang what's got her worse'n she ever has been. I wisht a starm would come up and blow the whole shooting-match of 'em clean to Roosia or wherever it is. Then they'd git enough o' them there heathen, I reckon. But they ain't got no right to interfere with me, not a bit. [*He puts a hand into his pocket and holds up a small tin box in his left hand and a plug of tobacco in his right.*] Here they come and set 'pon me about my tobacco. Chew chewing-gum, chewing-gum, they say, to save fer the heathen and to pertect my health. [*He rattles the tin box.*] And I've chewed that wad o' stuff till I cain't git rid of it in my sleep. Cain't wear it out, cain't by no means. I'm done of it, I am. Have to slip off and hide to chew my tobacco, and all in a land o' freedom. [*He stands thinking, then goes to the door at the left and calls.*] Mattie, air ye busy?

MATTIE
Yes, I've got my hands in the dough!

JERNIGAN
All right.

[*He stealthily bites off a chew from his plug, drops his tin box back in his pocket and spits in the fire with grim happiness. Just as he is leaning to spit a second time, the door opens suddenly at the left rear, and* MATTIE *comes in with a cloth. Old* JERNIGAN *draws back, and begins sweeping in a flurry of embarrassment. He calls out testily.*]

Thought you was busy. Ain't I doing all right?

MATTIE
Sweep it clean, Father. I forgot this cloth for the churn. [*She raises the lid from the churn and stirs the contents around with the dasher.*] It's all right and ready, lacking just a bit, for churning. Don't you let it slosh on anything while you're a-churning it.

[*She wraps the cloth around the handle of the dasher. The old man is sweeping and watching her out of the corner of his eye. While she is bent over she sees something on the hearth that attracts her attention. She rises up to her height and with a sharp note in her voice turns upon him.*]

Mr. Jernigan—

JERNIGAN
Nah, nah, Mattie.

MATTIE
Signs don't lie, and there's signs of it there on my hearth. [*Working around the room and watching him furtively.*] Right here in my front room! Ain't you got your mouth full of tobacco right this minute?

[*He shakes his head.*]

Yes, you have, yes, you have. [*She stands looking at him as he sweeps.*] Father, why don't you say something, cain't you talk?

[*He makes little movements of agony and finally chokes.*]

Yes, yes, you are chewing right now. Spit it out, spit it out! Don't stand there and swallow that juice, it'll kill you.

[*In desperation he runs to the fireplace and explodes into the fire, and stands coughing with a nauseated look on his face.*]

I'll get you some water! [*She hurries out and reappears immediately with a glass of water and a battered washbasin full of claying material.*] Here drink it, and take this pan and rag and clay the hearth over.

[*After drinking the water, he ruefully gets down on his knees and begins work. She goes to the machine.*]

Hurry and get it done, I got supper nearly cooked. [*She sits down and begins sewing and singing* "How firm a foundation——."]

JERNIGAN
[*Indicating the garments.*] Air they fer the heathen?

MATTIE
They are that.

JERNIGAN
[*Timidly.*] 'Course you know best, I reckon. But how you know they wear britches over there?

MATTIE
[*Staring at him in amazement.*] Who ever heard of folks not wearing britches! You know they'd put 'em in jail for such, if they didn't.

JERNIGAN
[*Venturing.*] I hearn they don't wear nothing over there but a string around their waist to tell where the middle is.

MATTIE
[*Pedaling furiously.*] You men don't care, of course, care 'bout nothing but your farming and your crops. Why, it's in the *Christian Herald* where the little children just go through the woods in big droves gnawing the bark off of

the trees they're so hungry. We've decided to give up our breakfast and send the cost of it to them.

JERNIGAN
That's why you didn't eat breakfast this morning. Well—you et a whole lot more fer dinner to make up fer it, didn't ye?

MATTIE
[*Sharply and with a nervous note in her voice as she gets suddenly up from the machine.*] Father, take all this mess out when you get done—that old 'simmon beer cup, and that old 'Manuel patent medicine bottle, and don't forget to carry the clay pan out——

[*She goes out at the left. Her song is heard rising in the distance. Old* JERNIGAN *continues claying the hearth, muttering to himself.* HENRY *comes in at the rear.*]

HENRY
[*Stretching his legs out carefully towards the fire.*] What's the matter with the hearth *now?*

JERNIGAN
[*Setting the pan in the corner by the wood-box.*] Nothing, nothing, Henry. She thought she saw a speck on it somewhere.

HENRY
You must a-been chewing tobacco ag'in.

JERNIGAN
Well, why shouldn't I chew it?

HENRY
Yeh, yeh, I wisht you could in peace.

JERNIGAN
You'd be better off ef you'd go back to chewing.

HENRY
I know. But I promised her I'd quit and I have.

JERNIGAN
I used to chew it 'fore it quit raining in Africky or wherever it is and 'fore old Bella Pate brung her sanctified self
around here, I did, and they was some joy in having a far
then, and some reason for having a farplace too. [*Tapping
on the andiron with his stick.*] That's what it's made fer—
to spet in.

HENRY
[*Timidly and somewhat hopefully.*] Why don't you talk it
out with Mattie. [*Earnestly.*] I wish you would.

JERNIGAN
Durned ef I didn't come purty nigh telling her something
a while ago. [*He catches* HENRY *by the arm.*] Now look-a
here, Henry, you'n me's got to do something. The thing
for you to do is to walk down the road tonight and meet
Mis' Pate and them folks and tell 'em they cain't come up
here to carry on no prayer-meeting and sewing business.
Tell 'em to go som'r's else. Tell 'em to go to—hell!

HENRY
[*Shrinking away.*] I cain't do that, I cain't. Lord, you're
near 'bout gone to cussing.

JERNIGAN
And tell 'em yer wife ain't gonna have nothing else to do
with sich.

HENRY
[*Quickly.*] I tell you what, you do it.

JERNIGAN
I would in a minnit, Henry, but you're the head o' the
house and you better, it's yer place to.

[HENRY *turns himself about before the fire.*]

HENRY
Mebbe they won't come tonight, and before they meet another time mebbe we can figger on something to do.

JERNIGAN
Hunh, they'll be hyuh, all right.

HENRY
[*Staring off.*] I hear they's mad dogs about. One bit at Dick Ryall's child this evening.

JERNIGAN
[*Studying.*] Well, that may break up the meeting, but I won't believe it till I see it, not me. Take more'n mad dogs to stop religion. You stand up to Mattie, I tell you, putt the britches on and wear 'em yourself. Lard, I cain't understand you. Why you let her impose on me in my old age the way you do I cain't see.

[*He turns away and sits down in his arm-chair.* MATTIE *comes in with a tin bucket in her hand.*]

MATTIE
I've got to go across the fields to Mis' Ragland's a bit—— [*Suddenly stopping.*] Henry, go right back out that door and wipe off your feet.

HENRY
[*Mumbling.*] I thought I cleaned my feet. [*He goes outside and is heard scraping his shoes on the edge of the porch.*]

MATTIE
Sweep it up, Father.

[*He gets the broom and sweeps.*]

I got to borrow some soda from Mis' Ragland and she wanted me to bring her a jar o' jam.

HENRY

[*Coming back into the room.*] I'll go over there for you, Mattie.

MATTIE

No, I'll go, and you-all go on and git your supper. I've put the biscuits in the stove, and they'll be ready by the time you wash and get to the table. Now Henry, don't let them biscuits burn. [*She goes out.*]

JERNIGAN

[*Scornfully.*] Jest look at her—didn't have a bit o' business over there, jest wants to go over see what old Nonie Ragland's got made up for the heathen. Henry, you got to lay the law down, I tell you.

HENRY

Yeh, yeh.

JERNIGAN

Now, I'm gonna talk straight to you. Women is like mules and all dumb brutes, Henry, you got to break 'em 'fore they'll work.

HENRY

Nah, nah, I cain't do that.

[*There is a knock on the porch.*]

JERNIGAN

Who kin that be? [*Happily.*] That's my doctor, I betcha.

[*The knock is repeated at the door.*]

HENRY

[*Raising his voice in sudden irritability.*] Go on away! Go 'way!

JERNIGAN

[*Staring at him.*] What—— Come in, come in!

[DOCTOR IMMANUEL *comes in.*]

I knowed it was you, doctor, I knowed it was you.

[*The* DOCTOR *is a man of medium height, about fifty years old, dressed in a cheap threadbare dark suit, celluloid collar and dark tie. His coat hangs low and nearly to the knees, clerical-like. Despite his cheap dress there is an indefinable air of distinction about him; something scholarly, something forlorn in his pale clean-cut face and dark piercing eyes. He carries a well-worn medicine case in his hand. As he enters the door, he pulls off his derby hat, disclosing a huge mop of long black hair streaked with gray and resting like a bolster on his neck and shoulders.*]

DOCTOR
[*In a deep level voice.*] Masters of this house, friends——

JERNIGAN
[*Pushing up a chair.*] Come right in, come right in and make yourself at home.

[*The* DOCTOR *lays his hat on the bed at the right and puts his case in a chair. He moves in a sort of dream-like, mask-like manner, intent upon his business and paying little attention to the two men.*]

DOCTOR
[*His voice moving in a level chant, half-singing as he opens his case.*] What can I do for you tonight? What can I do for you tonight? [*He takes out bottle after bottle, shakes it, squints at it towards the light, and replaces it, chanting as he does so.*]

> As you all know, wherever I go,
> My name is Immanuel,

I treat you well, I make you well,
Sound as the sweet church bell.

[*He turns suddenly on old* JERNIGAN *who starts back in surprise.*]

Now what is it, brother? What can I do for you?

JERNIGAN
[*Fetching his bottle.*] Another bottle. I just drunk the last.

HENRY
[*Growling.*] Another bottle of stump water, dishwater, rainwater.

DOCTOR
[*Holding up the bottle.*] Doctor Immanuel's Universal Remedy! Right it is and very fit. Distilled from secret weeds and herbs by mystic processes. Cures internal ailments, cuts, burns, bruises, is an antidote for poisons, can be taken internally or externally. For swelling in the joints, leg sores, sore throat, convulsions, dizziness, fits, and general disorders. [*The words roll from him in a flood. He turns towards old* JERNIGAN, *fixes him with his eyes, and suddenly sings out.*] What is your trouble, brother? Are you healed, better or—— It's cold tonight, cold tonight, and ice on the pools in the lane.

JERNIGAN
In my knee, you remember, in my knee. [*He slaps his hand to it.*] I'm getting better, doctor, slowly, slowly.

DOCTOR
[*Holding his hand up in assurance.*] Slowly but surely, certainly, absolutely. Another bottle and you walk straight as any man.

As you all know, wherever I go,
My name is Immanuel.

> I always make you well,
> As any man will tell. . . .

[*His voice drops to a whisper and he hums under his breath, the while he is putting away the empty bottle and getting out another. He hands the bottle to old* JERNIGAN.]

The price is one and a quarter now, brother. Prices have gone up, prices are going up. The demand exceeds the supply. [*Again he chants.*]

> I travel from morning till night
> Curing and fixing things right.
> From night until day
> I'm on a-my way——

[*He begins placing his bottles back in his case.*]

> Seeking the saddened sight——

[*Again he whirls upon the old man.*] Is the knee all that troubles you? Have you other troubles, diseases of the body or the soul?

JERNIGAN
[*Shaking his head quickly.*] Nanh, nanh, I'm all right saving my knee.

DOCTOR
[*Picking up a small bottle and holding it lovingly before him.*] Now here is a remedy, *the* remedy, the heart and soul of the matter, the help for the world's evils. Down in Egypt, the country of darkness, it was discovered. Dug out of the tombs of the powers of evil. Hid away they had it, but my agent discovered it, sent it to me, here it is. [*Reading.*] Dr. Immanuel's Egyptian Tonic.

[*Suddenly barking like an auctioneer, as* HENRY *jumps in his chair.*]

>Two dollars a bottle, two dollars,
>Going at two dollars.
>Are you weak and heavy laden,
>Sore distressed, sad distressed?
>It will cleanse of evil passion,
>Restore you bowels of compassion,
>Accidents, diseases chronic——

[*Shouting.*]

>The marvelous Egyptian Tonic.

[*He sticks it out at old* JERNIGAN.]

>Two dollars once, two dollars twice—
>Going at two——

JERNIGAN
[*Backing away from him as he fumbles in his pocketbook for his money.*] Nanh, nanh, this bottle's enough. Here's yer dollar and a quarter.

[*The* DOCTOR *takes the money impersonally.*]

Come up to the fire and warm yourself.

HENRY
[*Looking at old man* JERNIGAN *significantly.*] Anh-hanh, what'd I tell you?

[*The* DOCTOR *closes his case and goes to the bed for his hat.* HENRY *calls to him bitterly.*]

You better look out down in that creek for mad dogs.

DOCTOR
[*Turning back quickly but with dignity.*] Mad dogs?

HENRY
Yeh, dogs that are mad. Mad dogs. One of 'em bite you and you'll be madder'n you are now.

JERNIGAN
Yeh, you git bit and you'll foam at the mouth and gnaw

bedposts and cut up terrible like Sarah Williams done
'fore she died. She run out in the yard and screamed, and
they tried to ketch her but she run off and lay down by the
hedgerow and died biting her legs and arms and barking
like a dog.

DOCTOR

[*Quickly taking a tiny package from his case.*] Doctor
Immanuel's Mad Stone, good for all bites and poisons.
Bring it near the afflicted spot and it seizes upon it—
[*Clapping it to the top of his hand.*]—and sucks out the
poison. Five dollars apiece, five dollars. [*Gazing at it
fondly.*] This mysterious stone was taken from the belly of
a bewitched deer, killed by the old prophet of the Cape
Fear. [*Barking again.*] Five dollars apiece, five dollars,
going at five dollars. [*He pushes the stone quickly out at
old* JERNIGAN.]

JERNIGAN

Nanh, nanh, I ain't run mad.

DOCTOR

Five dollars— Five dollars once, five dollars twice— five
dollars——

[*Suddenly he stops and stares at* HENRY *as if perceiving
something remarkable and strange about him. He mechanically wraps up the stone and drops it back in the
case, never taking his eyes from the young man. He
moves toward him and walks obliquely around him.
Old* JERNIGAN *watches him with open mouth. As the*
DOCTOR *approaches him,* HENRY *turns and follows him
suspiciously with his eyes.*]

HENRY

Hyuh, hyuh, what you up to?

[*The* DOCTOR *continues to stalk him. He draws back
dramatically and points a sharp finger at* HENRY.]

DOCTOR
[*Grotesquely.*] Trouble.

JERNIGAN
[*Jumping and giggling nervously.*] Trouble, hee-hee!

HENRY
[*Staring at him.*] Trouble?

DOCTOR
[*His words beginning to pour out in a roll.*] I see upon that brow suffering. My name is Immanuel. I am needed, needed here and now. [*Looking at him in anguish.*] You are weak and heavy laden. Tell me. Speak forth your heart. I am come that ye might have rest from your suffering. Speak forth, thou unbeliever.

HENRY
Hyuh, hyuh, I ain't gonna have no monkey-shines. [*With a touch of entreaty in his voice.*] Stop it now.

DOCTOR
[*Shaking his head mournfully.*] I must help you. I feel the call of pain. Speak forth your heart.

HENRY
[*Turning towards old* JERNIGAN.] What's he up to nohow?

JERNIGAN
Now, now, you needn't ax me.

[*There is a long silence while the* DOCTOR *stares fixedly at* HENRY.]

HENRY
[*Looking anxiously about the room and presently bursting out.*] I tell you to stop looking at me thataway!

DOCTOR
Trouble, trouble, suffering in the countenance of that face! [*Imploringly.*] Speak, speak, I have remedy for suffering. I can help and aid thee.

[*He clasps his hands and waits.* HENRY *stirs uneasily in his chair and old* JERNIGAN *teeters nervously on his feet, beating his thighs with the back of his hands. At last old* JERNIGAN *explodes.*]

JERNIGAN

Well, you air in trouble, Henry!—In a way ye're in the deepest sort of trouble. [*Muttering.*] Me too, and me too.

DOCTOR

[*Triumphantly.*] Ah—hah! Speak, speak!

HENRY

[*Half in wrath and half in perplexed fear.*] Well, what'n the name of Old Scratch you want?

DOCTOR

Speak forth the evil that is possessing thee.

HENRY

[*Twisting about.*] You tell him, Pa, if they's any evil to be told.

JERNIGAN

Him and me's been seeing a right smart o' worry lately. We was talking about it before you come.

DOCTOR

I know, I perceive it.

JERNIGAN

[*Going on haltingly.*] As the scripture putts it, he's married to a wife. [*He stops.*]

DOCTOR

One had his land, one had his yoke of oxen, another had his wife. . . . As set forth in the gospel according to *Luke.*

JERNIGAN

[*Eagerly.*] That's it, doctor, his wife's tuk possession of everything hyuh.

HENRY
Now, now.

JERNIGAN
Well, she has. And that there doctor kin help you, I done told you he could. [*He steps nimbly out into the room and sweeps it with his arms.*] Look a' there, will you? Look at that there h'a'th. Clean as a sheet. And the floor and everything. A speck o' dirt got no home hyuh and we ain't nuther. [*Pointing to the sewing machine.*] And look over there at that there sewing. My good coat and britches gone fer good, all fer the heathen over the water.

HENRY
You mought stop trying to tell everything.

JERNIGAN
Well, you tell it then.

HENRY
Go on then and say what you wush.

JERNIGAN
All right and I will as shore as you're born. That's just it, doctor, she's plumb tuk with religion and sweeping and talking.

DOCTOR
Where is the lady of the house?

JERNIGAN
Off, off.

DOCTOR
A common case, a common case. The man must stand up and be the master. The scripture tells as much.

JERNIGAN
[*Jubilantly.*] There you air, Henry, there you air. [*Jerking

his thumb at HENRY.] But he won't, he won't, not him. He sets lak a wedge in the rain and takes it every bit. Big as a house he is and ain't got no backbone in him more'n a sack.

DOCTOR

Timid? Afraid? Lacking in manly courage?

HENRY

[*Wrathfully.*] Go on and have it your way!

DOCTOR

Doctor Immanuel will provide. He can cure.

JERNIGAN

You cure 'em both and I'll pay you. Fix it so's I kin chew my tobacco in peace and here's a five-dollar bill fer ye. [*He pulls out his pocketbook.*]

DOCTOR

I shall cure them, I must cure them, I *will* cure them. Amen!

JERNIGAN

Do that and this here's your'n.

[*He flaps a bill in his hands. The* DOCTOR *begins to pace up and down the room, pushing back his hair and mumbling to himself.*]

DOCTOR

[*Snapping.*] When will the lady of this house return?

HENRY

She just stepped acrost the field. But you needn't be planning none of your mess, I ain't gonna take no part in it.

DOCTOR

Mess! Mess! [*He resumes his walk.*]

JERNIGAN

[*Becoming excited.*] I dunno what you gonna do, Doctor, but I jest beccha you do it. [*Gleefully.*] I bet he does, Henry. Yeh, she'll be right back.

DOCTOR

No sooner said than done. [*Whirling upon* HENRY.] I can cure you both. I can bring peace and order into this distracted home. I can make a man of might out of you. I can make you a mighty man in Israel, both in deed and in word. I can bring back humility and love to the erring woman's heart. Yea, [*Lifting up his voice.*] I can prepare a proper helpmeet for you in your distress. [*Thundering and glaring.*] But—but—have you faith in my powers?

HENRY

I dunno—— I dunno—— Hah, crazy!

JERNIGAN

[*Ecstatically.*] Try to raise up yer faith, Henry. [*Grinding his hands in excitement.*] Hurry up, Henry, hurry up, she's gonna be back in a minute.

HENRY

[*Shaking his head weakly.*] I'm scared of all this business. How I know he won't kill me or something or hurt her.

DOCTOR

Kill! Hurt! [*His jaw falling open in amazement.*] Alas, young man, your words are wild, wild and full of poison to my kindly heart. [*His tone suddenly changes to anger.*] Take your own benighted way then. I offer you peace, you choose strife. So be it.

[JERNIGAN *grasps* HENRY'S *arm in supplication.*]

JERNIGAN

Henry, Henry, try it, try it, boy!

DOCTOR

[*Raising a warning hand.*] But listen, before I depart over the creek.—[*To himself.*] A mule there swelled with the colic—— Behold salvation is at hand and you refuse it.

JERNIGAN

Air ye crazy, Henry? There he is now going off.

HENRY

[*Beginning to show an unwilling interest under the* DOC-TOR'S *spell.*] Well,——

DOCTOR

[*Picking up his hat.*] I shall say no more.

JERNIGAN

Henry, Henry, don't let him go off like that there!

[*The* DOCTOR *picks up his case and moves towards the door.*]

HENRY

Well, if you're shore you won't hurt me ner her, I mought——

DOCTOR

[*Apparently no longer interested in him.*] Well, good night and may you endure your punishment as befits a sufferer so blind. [*He grasps the door knob.*]

JERNIGAN

Henry, Henry!

HENRY

Are you shore you won't hurt me?

DOCTOR

Faith! Have you faith?

HENRY

[*Standing up with sudden decision.*] Well, I'll try it then, by God! Where's your medicine? Bring it on.

[*With an amazingly agile bound the* DOCTOR *springs back into the room.*]

DOCTOR

Saved! Saved!

[*He opens his case and searches in its depths. Extracting*

two tiny bottles, he holds them up in his hands. HENRY
sits down again watching him with open mouth.]

Ah, here they are, Doctor Immanuel's Cure for the Unhappy Soul. The one is red, the other gray. The red is for
the rich blood of manhood. Drink it and you become
masterful, fearless, a tamer of the weaker sex. They will
bow down to you, worship you, feed upon your words of
wisdom as upon honey-dew. Let the woman drink the
gray and the man the red. He becomes the lord of his
house and his goods. She becomes the meek and lowly
helpmeet. There she sits by the fire silent, gentle and sweet.
There he sits her master, her lord.

JERNIGAN
[*His eyes shining.*] Listen at him, Henry, listen at him talk.

DOCTOR
[*Lifting up the red vial.*] I remember, I remember. I see in
the past. It is a night of storm. The moon is sick and pale
and wasting in the west.

> The pale moon doth rain,
> The red moon doth blow,
> It bringeth water in its beak.
> The white moon doth neither rain nor snow.

I rise up in my dreams. Doctor Immanuel comes forth
from his couch at the midnight hour, for now it is the time
to seek for the cure of unhappy souls. Silently I go through
the forest towards the appointed place. The rain and the
wind they comfort me on my journey. I go forth alone in
the forest, under the watchful heavens. The signs are right
in the sky, it is the time of the bull, and the bull means life
and more abundant life.

[*He waves his hands before his face and treads up and
down the room acting out his journey.* HENRY *and old*
JERNIGAN *stare at him as if mesmerized.*]

I go by the elder bush in the pathless swamp, I touch the sorrel tree, and place my hand upon the bark of the smooth bay tree. I mount the hill and taste of the sweet sassafras and a bit of the bitter pine, and I, Doctor Immanuel, as the cocks begin to crow, come to the place of the silent old man and he waits for me. He has had his dream. Together we go far to the east, he with six dried sticks of the bloody mulberry and I with six of the nameless bush under our arms. We come where the young strong man died for love and his rich red blood ran into the ground. There we set the pot and build the fire. [*His voice takes on a hypnotic monotone and he moves back and forth in the room with the queer unreal steps of a jumping-jack.*] And into the pot Doctor Immanuel casts his one and two and three. And likewise the silent one casts his one and two and three which shall not be named till time is done. The bottles are brought forth and filled. The silent old one to his home again which none but two can find. And Doctor Immanuel forth into the world to heal the distressed. [*His voice dies away and he hums to himself.*]

HENRY

[*Breaking from the spell.*] Ain't he crazy right?

DOCTOR

[*Picking up the gray vial and throwing up his hand.*] And hark! [*He stands with his hand uplifted, and they wait.*] It is night, a night of peace. The farmer sleeps his toil away, and the stock rest in the stall. The seeds wait in the earth, in the warm ground. The poor birds sit in the hedgerow and the snake goes not forth to prey. And now the old moon sleeps in the new moon's arms, hanging in the heavens above the three dark pines. [*Again he falls to striding up and down the floor.*] Doctor Immanuel is forth from his couch. The signs are right. The virgin walks in the sky. He comes to the three dark pines and waits in prayer. And the three maids of the deep swamp minister

unto him, they minister unto him. Out of the darkness
they come with song and with dancing, their heads hanging low and their rings shining and their garments flashing
silver with the flames of gold.

[*He turns and stares at* HENRY *who watches him grog-
gily.*]

From the mud of the turtle and the scaly snake they come,
rising out of the deep night time, out of the mire and
swampy slime, where the owl and the bat and the fever
are. They rise, bringing the cure, the gray cure, the draught
of humility, of peace. [*He stares at the gray vial and stands
lost in thought. Presently he turns, his voice humming.*]
Drink the red and be filled with life and power; drink the
gray, become the meek and gentle of the earth. Doctor
Immanuel has said his say!

[*He begins walking back and forth across the room.*
HENRY *and old* JERNIGAN *stare at him as if fascinated.
Far off a woman's voice is heard singing. It draws
nearer, and* MATTIE *passes around the house, singing
"Rescue the perishing," and goes into the kitchen.*]

HENRY
[*Swallowing hard.*] Hyuh, they's something quare!

JERNIGAN
He's gonna cure you, Henry. He is! Sink yer trust in him,
Henry!

DOCTOR
Come, drink the drink. [*He closes his case and sets the two
bottles on top of it.*] Call the lady of the house. She shall
have the gray.

HENRY
[*Starting from his dream, sidling up to the bottles, and
staring at them suspiciously.*] Mought be something in it,

mought not. [*A queer unreal smile breaks over his face
and he comes up to the* DOCTOR *and stares at him intently.*]
All right, dinged if I don't do it. Dinged if I don't!

[MATTIE'S *sharp insistent voice is heard in the kitchen.*]

MATTIE

Father! Fath-er-r! Henry! Henr-y!

JERNIGAN

Drink it, swallow it down, Henry! Can't be no worse'n
[*He turns and mocks* MATTIE.] "Father! Henry!" and
[*Singing.*] "Rescue the perishing——" Go on, Henry.

[HENRY *picks up the red vial, uncorks it and smells it
and sets it down, then takes up the gray one and does
likewise.*]

HENRY

Why it don't smell like nothing a-tall.

DOCTOR

[*Stopping in his walk and looking at him piercingly.*] Bid
the lady of the house come in.

HENRY

[*Throwing his head about and beating himself as if trying
to fight off the* DOCTOR'S *influence.*] You call her, Pa.

[*The door flies open at the left and* MATTIE *springs in
with a pan of burnt biscuits in her hands.*]

MATTIE

[*In a shrill nervous voice.*] Look what you've done, both of
you. I told you not to let the biscuits burn.

[JERNIGAN *looks at* HENRY *and* HENRY *looks at him.*]

JERNIGAN

[*Finally.*] I thought Henry was looking after them biscuits.

HENRY

[*Fumbling.*] I didn't even think of 'em, Mattie.

MATTIE

I know, I know. That's just the way it is. That's just the way it is. That's always the way it is.

DOCTOR

Madam, lady of this house!

MATTIE

[*Starting back.*] Oh, I didn't see you, Doctor 'Manuel. Put some wood on the fire, Father. When'd you come, Doctor 'Manuel?

DOCTOR

Madam, when you appeared in the door we were in the midst of a most momentous question.

MATTIE

What'n the world is all this to-do about? You'll have to tell it quick, I've got to hurry and get supper. We are sewing here tonight—[*With a weary, defiant look towards* HENRY *and old* JERNIGAN.]—sewing for the heathen.

DOCTOR

Madam, after tonight you will not bother about the heathen. You have enough trouble in your own household. We are solving that momentous question.

MATTIE

What in the world is all this to-do about, I ask you?

DOCTOR

[*With high dignity.*] Madam, behold the two bottles there. The one is red, the other gray. The red is for your husband, the gray for you.

MATTIE

Needn't think I'll drink any of your crazy mess.

DOCTOR

The husband will drink the red and take charge of his

household. You will drink the gray and obey him in what he says hereafter.

MATTIE

The Lord help my life! [*Turning to* HENRY.] Have you gone out'n your head same as him, to be taking on to such stuff?

HENRY

[*Timidly.*] Try and drink a little bit, Mattie. It won't hurt you! He says it's good for you.

MATTIE

The dog's foot!

HENRY

[*With a hint of determination in his voice.*] He's done said if I drink that stuff you won't know me for another man. [*Decisively.*] And I've said I'll drink it.

DOCTOR

He's going to drink his and you're going to drink yours.

MATTIE

That I'm not. I've never heard of such. Henry Jernigan, you must be crazy to fool with him.

HENRY

Yes, I'm gonna do it. I'm plumb tired of sich a mess of things. I'm gonna change it or die a-trying. [*With a lunge he grabs one of the bottles and throws the contents down his throat.*]

MATTIE

[*Screaming.*] Henry, it'll poison you!

[HENRY *stands tasting with his lips. A foolish smile breaks over his face.*]

HENRY

Why, it ain't no more'n—

[*The* DOCTOR *brings his hand down on* HENRY'S *shoulder with a whack and stares significantly at him.* HENRY'S *eyes gradually narrow in comprehension and he turns and walks back and forth across the room thinking. The* DOCTOR *moves around as if unconcerned. Suddenly* HENRY *springs into the air with a yell. Old* JERNIGAN *starts back and falls over a chair.*]

JERNIGAN
Lard, Lard a-mercy!

MATTIE
[*Running up to* HENRY.] Henry, Henry, honey, what is it?

HENRY
[*Tearing wildly around the room and shrieking.*] I'm pizened, pizened! Help, water, I'm afar inside.

[He doubles over in pain. MATTIE *pursues him wringing her hands. All the while the* DOCTOR *walks ecstatically and yet unconcerned around the room, carrying on his automaton-like actions and his monologue.*]

DOCTOR
[*Chanting.*]

> As you all know, wherever I go,
> My name is Immanuel.
> I treat you well, I make you well,
> As sound as the sweet church bell.
> Down the road I travel,
> Going in rain or shine,
> Healing the sick and afflicted,
> No medicine like unto mine.
> This I tell who comes like Immanuel.

HENRY
[*Falling into a chair and slobbering heavily at the mouth as he gasps.*] Pizened! Pizened! Help, water! [MATTIE *throws her arms around his neck.*]

MATTIE

Run, Father, run and bring the bucket of water.

[*The old man shoots into the kitchen and back like a streak. All the while* MATTIE *is crooning over* HENRY *and rubbing his face and forehead feverishly.*]

Oh, darling, honey. What can I do? [*She breaks into wild sobs.*]

JERNIGAN

Hyuh, hyuh, drink some water, Henry.

[HENRY *springs out of his chair, knocking* MATTIE *from him. He souses his head in the bucket and drinks, spits out great mouthfuls of water on the floor and empties the bucket over his head. Then he stamps the bucket to pieces, shrieking and yelling.*]

MATTIE

Run for the doctor, run for the doctor!

DOCTOR

I am Doctor Immanuel at your service, madam.

[MATTIE *turns and glares at him a moment and slaps him in the face.* HENRY *snatches up the broom and begins chasing the* DOCTOR *around the room and beating him. The* DOCTOR *makes an effort to get his case and hat as he is pursued, calling out.*]

This is wrong, wrong! Ye do not understand.

[*He opens the door and flees into the night.* HENRY *falls into a chair and rocks back and forth, groaning and moaning.* MATTIE *comes sobbing up to him.*]

HENRY

[*Whirling and seizing* MATTIE *by the throat.*] Who are you? I know: Mattie. You sew for the heathen and worry your husband's life out about dirt. Now in the grave they'll be plenty of dirt. And you sing, and you sing; and you talk and you talk. [*He grabs the remaining bottle and uncorks it.*] Drink this here bottle o' stuff.

MATTIE

[*Clenching her teeth and fighting back.*] I won't, I won't! It'll poison me, it'll kill me!

HENRY

[*Pulling open her mouth and pouring the contents in.*] Nunh—unh, I reckin it won't!

[*She swallows and coughs and strangles, then drops to the floor crying.* HENRY *strides about the room kicking the furniture to pieces and throwing out his shoulders and shouting.*]

I'm a new man, a man o' might, a he-man in Israel! [*Turning upon* MATTIE.] And you have drunk the drink. You gonna be humble down, a help-mate. [*He drops back in his chair in a dying posture.*]

MATTIE

Oh, Henry, Henry, baby!

HENRY

When I'm gone, take care of Pa. Let him live in peace. Let him have his tobacco and spet in the far.

[MATTIE *crawls on her knees before him and lays her head in his lap, weeping.*]

MATTIE

Get the doctor, Father. Hitch up and go for the doctor.

[*Old* JERNIGAN *starts for the door.* HENRY *jumps up and snatches him back.*]

HENRY

You ain't, you ain't. Let me die in peace.

[*There is the sound of a medley of voices outside. Women gabbling in excitement.* MATTIE *climbs up to her feet and runs to the door.*]

MATTIE

Is that you, Mis' Bella? Come here, come here quick.
Henry's poisoned and he's a-dying.

[*The gabble and excitement outside increases. A* VOICE
replies from the yard.]

VOICE

I'm coming, Mattie, I'm coming.

[*She is heard coming up on the steps.* HENRY *gets up
from his chair and begins to bark like a dog, blubbering
and growling.*]

HENRY

[*Shrieking again.*] I' been bit by a mad dog. [*He barks.*]

VOICE

Lord a-mercy, he's run mad!

[*A low murmur of horror rises from the women outside,
followed by shrieks and then the sound of running feet.*
HENRY *rushes out of the door barking and pursuing
them.*]

MATTIE

[*Looking at old* JERNIGAN *through her tears.*] He ain't
been bit by no mad dog!

JERNIGAN

[*Stuttering with excitement.*] Mebbe that's the way the
pizen works. That doctor said he got it a quare way in the
middle of the night and a storm on and a' old man helping
him.

MATTIE

He's crazy. [*Wringing her hands.*] Why'd you let him give
Henry that stuff? The mess I took won't nothing, weak as
water! [*She goes to the door calling piteously.*] Henry!
Henry!

[*Old* JERNIGAN *comes up to the bottle she has dropped and looks at it.*]

JERNIGAN
[*With a shout.*] He's tuk the wrong medicine, Mattie! He tuk that there gray stuff and you tuk the red!

MATTIE
[*At the door.*] Henry! Henry!

[HENRY *comes back on the porch and gives a farewell bark.* MATTIE *runs out and throws her arms around him. He flings her from him and strides into the room. His shoes are covered with mud. He goes to the fireplace and stamps it off on the hearth.*]

JERNIGAN
[*Running up to him excitedly.*] Hyuh, hyuh, you tuk that gray stuff. Look, look!

HENRY
[*Waving him off.*] It don't make no difference. 'Twon't nothing but water.

[MATTIE *comes in and stares at him as he casually cleans his boot on the hearth.*]

MATTIE
[*Whimpering.*] What's happened, Henry? You seem——

HENRY
I been cured, that's what. The medicine done it. [*He gets up, looks around the room, goes over to the machine, gathers up the clothes for the heathen, picks out a coat and trousers and throws them at the old man.*] Here, there's your Ransome Taylor coat and your britches. The heathen ain't gonna git 'em.

calmly goes to his chair and sits down. MATTIE *has been looking on a moment and then with a glad cry of com-*
[*He wipes his shoes with the other garments and then*

*prehension falls on her knees by him and lays her head
sobbing in his lap.*]

J E R N I G A N
[*Dropping in his chair thunderstruck.*] Well, I be durned if
I ever seed the beat!

[*He thinks a moment, and then bursts out in a low
musical chuckle. His face spreads into a grin that breaks
over his face in a thousand wrinkles. He cuts a caper on
the floor, stopping now and then trying to comprehend
what has happened.* HENRY *sits solemnly stroking* MAT-
TIE'S *head. The door is cracked open at the rear and*
DOCTOR IMMANUEL *pokes his head in.*]

D O C T O R
Masters of this house——

H E N R Y
[*Turning and snarling.*] Hanh—Scat! [*He barks and the*
DOCTOR *slams the door. After a moment* HENRY *calls old*
JERNIGAN.] Pa, go and tell him to come in and get his hat
and case.

[MATTIE'S *sobs gradually die away.*]

Yeh, I know, poor child. I did scare you, didn't I?

[*Only a whimper from* MATTIE *and hugging of* HENRY'S
knees answer him.]

J E R N I G A N
[*At the door.*] Come on in, doctor, and get yer stuff. He
ain't gonna hurt you.

[*The* DOCTOR *comes gravely in and gets his case and hat.*]

H E N R Y
Pa, give him that five dollars.

J E R N I G A N
[*His sides shaking with enjoyment.*] Hyuh, hyuh, it is. You
done it, Doc, same as you said you would.

HENRY

And you needn't come back. I don't need you! [*He lifts his head with decision written on his face.*] Lemme have a look at the plug of tobacco, Pa.

DOCTOR

[*At the door.*] Remember that I am always at your service. Peace abide with you and this house always. I am on my way now to another patient.

HENRY

That's all right, doctor. You needn't bother about us. We ain't gonna need you no more. Are we, Mattie?

[MATTIE *shakes her head.*]

DOCTOR

[*Going out.*]

> As you all know, wherever I go,
> My name is Immanuel.

[*He closes the door and his chant dies away in the night.*]

HENRY

I said, Pa, I'd like a look at that tobacco.

MATTIE

[*Raising her head.*] Don't you spit on——

HENRY

[*Crushing her back on the floor.*] Nanh, nanh, I tell you I been cured. I'm boss. [*Breaking into a loud roaring laugh.*] Hooray! Hooray! I'm another man. I'm cured, I'm boss. Gimme that 'backer.

[*The old man hands it to him eagerly.* HENRY *bites off an enormous chew and hands the plug back. Old* JERNIGAN *hesitates a moment and then also bites off a mouthful. A look of deep content comes over him. He snuggles into a chair and chews.* HENRY *chews. They look across at each other.* HENRY *signifies to the old*

man with a motion of his hand that he spit first. Old
JERNIGAN *with signs refuses.* HENRY *spits profusely and
loud in the direction of the fire. Old* JERNIGAN *does
likewise.*]

JERNIGAN
[*Eyeing* HENRY *slyly, as he rolls his tobacco sweetly in his
mouth.*] Hee—hee!

[MATTIE *sits hugging* HENRY'S *knees.*]

HENRY
[*Nodding happily and wisely.*] Unh-hunh-yeh. [*They sit
saying nothing. Presently* HENRY *looks over at the old man
and laughs suddenly and deeply.*]

JERNIGAN
What?

HENRY
I run them there women right into the mudhole out there.

JERNIGAN
[*Beating his thigh gleefully.*] Hee-hee! Hee-hee!

HENRY
I shore did.

[*They lapse into silence. By this time* MATTIE *has somewhat raised her head and is staring contemplatively by*
HENRY'S *chin into the fire.*]

JERNIGAN
[*Shivering a bit and stirring the fire.*] Gonna be cold
Henry, cold.

HENRY
Yeh.

JERNIGAN
Robins been flying towards the South all day.

[*They both lean towards the fire and spit.*]

PARENTS
ARE PEOPLE

By M. Jerry Weiss

From Guidance Through Drama, *by M. Jerry Weiss, copyright 1951, 1952, 1954 by M. Jerry Weiss, by permission of Whiteside, Inc.*

All rights reserved.

CAST

Sylvia Donlevy, mother, about 42
Bill Donlevy, father, about 46
Carol Donlevy, daughter, about 20
Mike Donlevy, son, about 17
Les Donlevy, son, about 9
Mrs. Herbertson, neighbor, about 38
Jimmy Herbertson, son, about 9

Y

T ———— p

B

X

A

C

Z

Key to stage diagram:

X—*Door to bedroom*
  and bathroom
Y—*Door to kitchen*
Z—*Door to outside corridor*

A, B, C—*Chairs*
T—*Table*
On table (p)—*Phone*

As the curtain rises, SYLVIA *comes to the phone. The scene is a small apartment. There are three doors—*X, Y, Z. *The* Y *door leads to the kitchen; the* Z *door leads to the outside corridor. The* X *door leads to the bedrooms. The apartment is moderately furnished. No one else is in the room.* SYLVIA *is in a housecoat.* DIRECTION: *Phone is ringing as curtain rises.*

SYLVIA

[*Enters from* X, *sits at* B.] Never mind, darling, I have it. [*In phone.*] Hello . . . Yes . . . Oh, no . . . you just can't. . . . I see. . . . What's the matter with Tommy? . . . That's awful. . . . Well, worrying won't help. . . . Kids get over temperatures real soon. . . . Yes . . . You don't know how much I counted on you, Mrs. Joyce. . . . Oh, I thought you knew. Bill's got a special lodge meeting tonight. Installation. He was elected Keeper of the Archives. . . . Yes, I think it's pretty fine, too. . . . Yes, I was going along for the dinner and party. . . . Oh, well . . . I certainly hope Tommy gets better soon. . . . Good-by.

[*Pause for 10 seconds before doorbell rings.*]

BILL

[*Off stage.*] Never a dull moment—who's coming at this hour?

SYLVIA

[*Rises and crosses* Z.] I'm on my way—— [*Opens door.*] Carol!

CAROL
[*In coat and carrying suitcase.*] Hi, Mom!

SYLVIA
For goodness' sake! Come on in.

[*As they enter both crossing to center stage.*]

What's wrong, darling? Tell me quickly! What's happened?

CAROL
What's wrong? You know perfectly well what's wrong!

BILL
[*Entering from* x.] Is that Carol?

CAROL
Hi, Dad.

BILL
Hello, dear. What's happened?

CAROL
As if you didn't know. Why did you write that I couldn't go to the Mercury Dance?

SYLVIA
So that's why you came all the way in from school—just about the dance.

CAROL
[*Turning to* SYLVIA.] Just about the dance she says! Well, that's just about as important to me as anything in the world. All the boys picked me to be Venus. [*To* BILL.] Why, why can't I go?

BILL
For a simple reason. Listen, darling. We just can't afford it now. Figure it out for yourself. You want a new formal for it. Your fare—expense money while you're there. Any

way you look at it, it'll cost $200. We can't spend $200 for a weekend.

CAROL
But, Dad . . .

SYLVIA
[*Interrupting.*] Carol—listen, let's skip it for tonight. You remember that Daddy was elected Keeper of the Archives at his lodge, and tonight's the big dinner and installation.

BILL
It's a big honor, too. So what do you say we talk tomorrow?

CAROL
O.K. But I'm not going back to school till we get this settled. [*Picks up suitcase and on exit.* . . .] I might as well put my stuff away. [*Exits* x.]

BILL
What are we going to do about her? If she feels this way about the Mercury Dance, what'll she say about having to finish up at the local college next year?

SYLVIA
[*Sits at* c.] I don't know. We'll have to break it to her gently. But she'll have to agree. Mike's graduating from high school and he's all set for pre-med. It's the only thing that might save him from being drafted.

BILL
I wish we could be sure of that.

SYLVIA
Well, most pre-med students are exempted, or deferred or something, and he's always wanted to be a doctor. Carol will understand it's more important for her brother to go away to school. After all, she's had two years away. She can finish up here.

BILL

I hate to do it to her. . . . Gosh it's after six and you're still in your housecoat. We ought to be on our way.

SYLVIA

[*Rises.*] Darling—I'm awfully sorry, but I'm afraid you'll have to go alone.

BILL

What's the matter now? Buck up—Carol will get over it.

SYLVIA

It's nothing to do with her, Bill. It's just that—it was Mrs. Joyce who called a few minutes back.

BILL

[*Crosses to phone book on table.*] Oh-oh! We haven't any baby sitter.

SYLVIA

You guessed it. Her Tommy's running a temperature. So, of course, she can't sit with Les. And Mike has tickets for a basketball game and a date to take to it. I can't ask him to stay with Les now. And who can I get the last minute?

BILL

[*Thumbing through phone book.*] Well, I was looking for Mrs. Turner's number . . . but, Carol's home now.

SYLVIA

I don't know. I hate to ask her. She probably made a date on the way in.

BILL

I'll ask her. I bet she'll stay. [*Calling.*] Carol?

CAROL

[*Enters from x.*] Yes, what is it?

BILL

You'll stay with Les, won't you?

CAROL
What?

SYLVIA
[*Rises.*] You see, the lady who was supposed to sit with him can't make it.

BILL
And I want Mother to be with me. This is my big night.

CAROL
Oh, O.K. I'll stay.

SYLVIA
[*Crosses to* CAROL.] Well, come along to the kitchen and I'll show you what I have for the kids' supper and you can tell me all about school.

[SYLVIA *and* CAROL *exit.* BILL *stands straightening tie, and* LES *and* MIKE *enter front door.*]

LES
Aw, you cheated.

MIKE
Sez who? Hi, Pop. Wow . . . look at the slick Lady Killer.

[LES *and* MIKE *take off their jackets and throw them on a chair.*]

LES
[*Crossing to* A.] Hey, did you hear about the murder in the park yesterday?

BILL
What murder?

LES
[*Sits at* A.] Well, Johnny Furman came to school today and told us all about the knifing and there were lots of cops and everything. It was really bloody. . . . Sure wish I could have been there.

MIKE
[*Sits on arm of* C.] And what would you have done?

LES
I'd use my Dick Tracy fingerprint set and I bet I'd have
caught the guy who done it.

[SYLVIA *re-enters from* Y. *She leans over* LES *and rumples his hair.*]

SYLVIA
You'd catch who, who done what?

LES
The murderer. . . .

BILL
[*Crossing to left and sits at* C *while* MIKE *gets up.*] One of
your sons has a strong interest in bloody murders.

MIKE
And it's not me.

LES
No. You're only interested in girls and chemistry.

MIKE
What else is there?

CAROL
[*Enters from* Y, *stands behind* A.] Lots of things. Clothes,
jewelry, and nice things. . . . Gentlemen. . . .

MIKE
If the prima donna isn't back again, blessing her happy
household. What brings you home? Money again?

CAROL
It's none of your business.

MIKE
The only time you come home is to get money or . . .

SYLVIA

Children, now stop this at once! Mike, you and Les go get washed. Carol is going to give you supper tonight.

[MIKE *and* LES *on slow exit.*]

MIKE

She'll probably try and poison us.

[*Exit* MIKE *and* LES X.]

CAROL

You think that's a bad idea?

LES

[*Sticking his head out of the door* X.] But I'd know it was you and I'd catch you.

SYLVIA

Go ahead, Carol dear, to the kitchen. If you need me call me. I want to finish dressing.

[CAROL *exits to kitchen* Y.]

BILL

[*Reading paper.*] What a family! They all love each other so much. Have you ever seen such brotherly-sisterly love?

SYLVIA

[*On exit* X.] Brotherly love is O.K. But sisterly . . . I don't know.

[LES *enters from* X.]

LES

Hey, Pop. Where you going all dressed up?

BILL

Your Mother and I are going out to dinner.

LES

[*Picks up comic book at table.*] Well, Mike's going out, too.

Who's going to be home with me?

BILL
Carol will be here.

LES
[*Sits at* A *and is reading book.*] That's what I asked, who
will be here?

BILL
Don't you like your sister, Les?

LES
[*Still reading.*] She's O.K., I guess, if you like *girls*. I just
don't like them. They cry at the littlest things.

BILL
Well, your mother is a girl, and she doesn't cry at the
littlest things.

LES
She's different. I like Mom.

BILL
Well, you should like your sister, too.

LES
I suppose I like her better than I do any other girls. Just
a little bit better anyway. But I don't like any other girls.

BILL
Why don't you like Carol?

[MIKE *enters from* X *and interrupts.*]

MIKE
I know why Les doesn't like Carol. For lots of reasons.
Since she's been away at school she's changed too darn
much. She's snobbish and thinks she owns the world or
something. She puts on a big act as though she's "It."

[CAROL *enters from* Y.]

CAROL
Do you guys want to eat?

LES
[*Drops book.*] I do. [*Exits fast* Y.]

MIKE
If her highness doesn't mind serving the caviar before the cocktails, I think I might make it. [*Exits* Y.]

CAROL
Her highness isn't going to wait forever to please King Tut. [*Exits* Y.]

[SYLVIA *enters from* X *dressed for the meeting.*]

SYLVIA
Well, how do you like it? [*Turning around.*]

BILL
I've never seen you look lovelier. Darling, you're prettier than the night I fell in love with you.

SYLVIA
And stouter, too. You don't know how much trouble I had to fix this dress so it would fit.

BILL
I thought you were going to get a new dress?

SYLVIA
Well, it's just one of those things. I went downtown to look at something new and everything cost so much. . . .

BILL
But, you haven't bought anything for yourself in a long time.

SYLVIA
I know, dear. But with Carol at school and with Michael

next year . . . Bill, we go out so little, and I just couldn't
see putting all that money into a new dress when this one
could serve the same purpose, with a little fixing.

BILL

So, you look more wonderful. [*Kisses her.*] Now wait here
a minute.

[*He exits z and she checks her hairdo.* BILL *enters with
a florist box containing a corsage.*]

BILL

Here, dear, something for you.

SYLVIA

Bill, you shouldn't have. [*Excitedly opens the box.*] I
haven't gotten a corsage in ages. . . . I love it. It's beautiful.

BILL

[*Modestly.*] I'm sorry it's not an orchid, but maybe some
day.

SYLVIA

It's the most beautiful corsage I've ever had. I'll keep it in
the box until we get to the Lodge so nothing will happen
to it. . . . Say, maybe we ought to go out more often . . .
and then I would get more corsages. . . .

BILL

You know, Sylvia, I've been thinking a lot about that. We
just don't seem to get out any more. We ought to go out
lots.

SYLVIA

[*Putting hat on.*] Yes, and who would stay with Les? With
baby sitters costing so much, we wouldn't have any money
to spend if we did go out. Besides, I like being home with
my husband.

BILL

Well, why couldn't Mike stay home with Les?

SYLVIA

He has homework to do, and he can't keep an eye on Les and try to study, too. With the draft situation as it is, I just don't feel right in trying to get him to stay in the few free evenings he has.

BILL

Well, I'll get our coats. Are you ready? [*Exits* z.]

SYLVIA

Yes, dear. Bring my scarf, too, please.

[MIKE *bursts into room from* Y, *sandwich in hand.*]

MIKE

[*At table.*] Golly, I'm late. I can't find my tickets. I promised Barbara I'd pick her up by eight and it's six-thirty already . . . and I haven't showered, shaved, or anything else yet.

[CAROL *enters angrily from* Y.]

CAROL

Michael Donlevy, you come back here and finish eating. You can't carry food all through the house for me to clean up.

[MIKE *exits* X *and ignores her.*]

SYLVIA

Oh! let him go, Carol. Barbara is the only thing he has on his mind.

CAROL

Barbara who?

SYLVIA

Barbara Kingston. You know her. . . .

CAROL

That freckled-face drip . . . buck teeth and braces. . . .

[MIKE *enters with shirt off, shaving brush in hand.*]

MIKE

[*Shakes shaving brush at* CAROL.] She's prettier than you are and a heck of a lot nicer, too. She doesn't go around showing off and putting on airs and . . . [*Pushes shaving brush in her mouth then runs off* X.]

[BILL *enters carrying coats and scarf.*]

CAROL

Go slit your throat! [*Stomps off* Y.]

BILL

[*Helps* SYLVIA *into coat.*] Really, Mrs. Donlevy, those children of yours!

SYLVIA

Of mine! Let me see if Les is all right.

[*Starts to door when* LES *enters from* Y.]

LES

[*Sits at* A.] If I'm not here when you get back, look for me in the closest river. Carol might have dragged me there. And have Inspector Thompson drag the river for my body.

BILL

You know Carol wouldn't do a thing like that to you unless you were pretty bad.

LES

You can't tell about girls. They're a funny lot. All they like is kissing and crying.

BILL

Well, you kiss your mom and dad good night and promise to be a good boy.

LES
[*Rises.*] I'll try. [*Kisses them good-by.*]

SYLVIA
Good night, Mike, have a nice time. Good night, Carol dear.

MIKE
[*From* x.] Good night, Mom and Dad. . . . Have a wonderful time.

BILL
Thanks, feller.

CAROL
[*Calling from kitchen.*] Good-by.

[BILL *and* SYLVIA *exit.* LES, *left alone in the living room, sprawls out on the floor and starts reading the newspaper. He soon gets tired, and then goes to phone. He dials number, and. . . .*]

LES
[*Sits at* B.] Hello . . . Mrs. Herbertson, is Jimmy there? . . . Yes, please. . . . Hello, Jimmy, this is Secret Service 1009 talking. . . . I can't talk loud because someone might hear me. . . . Can you come over for a little while tonight? . . . The folks have gone out and just Carol is here. We can decode and things, just so long as we don't make too much noise. O.K. I'll wait. . . . Tell her you'll come home early. . . . [LES *looks around to make sure no one is listening.*] Yeah . . . you can! . . . Swell! . . . O.K. I'll be looking for you in about ten minutes. [*Hangs up and picks up comic book from table.*]

[*Enter* CAROL *from* Y.]

CAROL
[*Sits at* A.] When Mike gets out of the shower, you go ahead and take one. Then put on your pajamas, and you

can sit up awhile in here and read the comics or listen to the radio.

LES

Aw, shower! I can't right now. Jimmy Herbertson is coming over for a little while to see me about something important.

CAROL

What's so important that he can't see you in your pajamas?

LES

You know it isn't nice to have company and you be in pajamas. How would you feel if someone came up to see you and you were in pajamas?

CAROL

That's different. Anyhow—what's so important that's bringing Jimmy over here tonight?

LES

It's something. . . . School work.

CAROL

All right, but you're not going to stay up too late, so don't try to stall for time. You know how Mrs. Herbertson is about her darling Jimmy. He'll have to go home early.

LES

I know.

CAROL

Les, whatever happens don't grow up to be like Mike— he's awful.

LES

Why?

CAROL

For one thing he has no respect for me. And I'm older.

LES
Maybe that's because you're a girl. I don't like girls either.

CAROL
Don't you like me?

LES
I suppose so. You're my sister. . . .

[CAROL *exits laughing* X. *Doorbell rings.* LES *goes* Z.
There stands JIMMY *carrying a briefcase which contains
his books.*]

LES
Password.

JIMMY
Miracle Murder Mystery.

LES
[*Walking to center stage.*] Enter.

JIMMY
[*Walking to center stage.*] Where's everybody?

CAROL
[*Calling from offstage.*] Who is there, Les?

LES
Just Jimmy.

JIMMY
Did you see the new *Mystery Comics* yet? It's swell.
There's a story in there about a guy who has died and
then comes back to life and starts killing all the people in
a small village. [*Runs around impersonating a machine-
gun and falls into chair* C.]

LES
That's nothing. *Gigantic Torture* has a swell new story in
it. This guy is caught by the Indians and they have him

hanging from a tree and they're going to build a fire under him and . . . [*Whirls about with swishing noises. Phone rings*—LES *answers.*]

LES

Oh, nuts! Hello. Yes, Carol is here. . . . One minute please. [*Calling.*] Carol, telephone.

[CAROL *enters from* X. LES *goes and sits on arm of chair* C.]

CAROL

Hello, Jimmy. Thank you, Les. [*Goes to phone—sits at* B.]

LES

[*Whispering to* JIMMY.] I told Carol that you came over to do school work. Let's get out the arithmetic or something.

JIMMY

Sure. [*Goes over and takes book from briefcase and returns to* C.]

CAROL

[*On phone.*] Hello! Oh, yes, Anne. . . . Gee, it's wonderful to hear your voice again. . . . What are you doing home from school? . . . Oh, Rod Dickinson . . . sure, I remember him. . . . He's got a new car? . . . Well, you don't say. . . . When were you two pinned? . . . Wonderful. . . . Lots of luck. . . . Oh, I just came in from college for the weekend. . . .

[LES *and* JIMMY *sit talking.* MIKE *comes to the door, buttoning his shirt and cuffs and yells.* . . .]

MIKE

[*At* X.] I hope you go back sooner. . . .

CAROL

What? . . . Well, I don't think so. . . .

MIKE

[*Mocks her.*] What? . . . Well, I don't think so. . . .

CAROL

Well, my mother and father have gone out for the evening and I'm playing baby sitter for the night. . . . Oh, I'd really love to go for a ride . . . but I'm afraid I can't make it tonight. . . . Who did you say was there?

MIKE

The way you said that I'd swear it was Van Johnson himself. [MIKE *leaves and slams door to bedroom.*]

CAROL

The All-American? . . . And he needs a date? . . . Oh, darn my luck. . . . Of all nights. . . . Just wait a minute will you, Anne? [*Puts down phone and starts talking to* LES *and* JIMMY.]

CAROL

Les, if I went out for a little while, and promised to bring each of you an ice cream cone, would you be too scared to stay here?

LES

[*With glee.*] No. Will you bring me chocolate?

JIMMY

I want strawberry.

CAROL

O.K. But don't say anything about this in front of Mike.

LES *and* JIMMY
[*Together.*] O.K.

CAROL

[*Goes back to phone.*] I think I might be able to go out for just a little while, if you promise not to stay away too long. That will be swell. How about thirty minutes. . . . Fine. . . . I'll look for you then. . . . Oh, listen . . . I'll meet you downstairs. O.K. See you soon. . . . Thanks for calling . . . good-by. [*Hangs up.*]

[MIKE *enters in coat ready to leave.*]

MIKE
I hope you have a wonderful time torturing the little ones.
. . . I couldn't think of anything crueler than the idea of
you pretending to be a mother.

CAROL
Oh, turn blue!

MIKE
[*On quick exit* z.] So long, kids.

BOYS
'By, Mike.

CAROL
[*Rises and starts* x.] I'm going to fix my face and then I'm
going out for a little while.

LES
[*Following her.*] Don't forget the ice cream.

JIMMY
[*Following* LES.] I want strawberry.

CAROL
[*On exit* x.] And you two must promise not to tell Mom or
Dad anything about me going out. Is that fair? [*Exits.*]

LES
[*Calling.*] Fair and square. You know, Carol, you're not
half bad sometimes.

JIMMY
[*Facing* LES.] What are we going to do now?

LES
I'll get my arithmetic book and we can pretend we're
doing that, and then Carol won't know any different. But
let's make up code messages we can send to each other.

JIMMY
[*Crosses and sits at* B.] O.K. Let's work on that table.

LES
[*Sits on table.*] Right, chief. You want to listen to the radio?

JIMMY
What's on?

LES
I think "The Dead Stiff" comes on in a little while. Do you ever listen to that?

JIMMY
I used to, but Mom wouldn't let me because I'd have such terrible dreams.

LES
I used to have nightmares, but now I only have them when I see a real scary movie. Did you see that Western that was on at the State last Saturday?

JIMMY
[*Imitating scalping.*] The one about the Indian girl who scalped her white man husband?

LES
Yeah. . . . Wasn't that good?

JIMMY
Boy, what a raid they had. . . . Did you ever see so many Indians in all your life?

LES
I wish I was a cowboy in those times. I really would have killed a lot of Indians I bet.

JIMMY
[*Getting excited—jumps up and goes through motion of Indian.*] Yeah. That was the life. . . . Then remember

how that old Indian brought out that knife and was going
to slice Rex Bitter to pieces. . . .

LES

[*Jumps down.*] Yeah . . . and then Rex's horse started to
jump on him from behind. . . . I sure would have hated
to be that Indian and have a horse jumping all over
me. . . .

[*The boys go through some of the movie action—knock
over chair.* CAROL *enters from* x—*dressed to go out.*]

CAROL

[*Picking up chair.*] Hey—cut out that racket. I thought
you two were going to behave. I'm going now. I'll see you
two in a little while, O.K.?

LES

Sure. Don't forget the ice cream.

CAROL

And don't forget you promised not to tell Mom and Dad
anything.

LES

Sure, sure. 'By.

CAROL

'By. And be good boys. [CAROL *exits* z.]

LES

[*Sits at* A.] Hey, what about the codes we started before?
Got anything ready yet?

JIMMY

[*Sits at* B.] Nope. Are you using the numbers or the alpha-
bet?

LES

I'm using the numbers. It's easier.

JIMMY

I am, too. I'll be through in a minute.

LES

O.K. You finish and I'll go get something I want to show you.

[JIMMY *keeps writing and* LES *exits* X.]

JIMMY

[*Talking as he writes.*] 2-5-23-1-18-5. [*Calling.*] O.K., Les . . . all through.

[LES *enters with a cap pistol that is loaded with caps.*]

LES

Isn't it a beaut? Mike gave it to me last week for my birthday.

JIMMY

[*Taking it in his hands.*] It sure is. I bet it cost a dollar anyway.

LES

More than that. Try pulling the trigger.

JIMMY

[*Shooting pistol.*] It's so easy. I think this is nicer than Dicky Harris's pistol.

LES

Me, too. Where's your message?

JIMMY

Here. Where's yours?

LES

[*Hands him piece of paper.*] Here.

[JIMMY *reads the letter slowly . . . as if deciphering is difficult.*]

JIMMY

T-A-K-E. . . . That's take . . . M-O-N-E-Y. Take money . . . T-O . . . That's to . . . X-621 . . . Say, let's play cowboy and Indians some more.

LES

O.K.

JIMMY

[*Rising excitedly.*] I want to be the cowboy and use the gun. [*Shoots more caps.*]

LES

I got another cap pistol I'll use. [*Starts x then stops.*] Maybe we shouldn't shoot them off in the house?

JIMMY

Who's here to stop us? Nobody will know.

LES

O.K. I'll get it. [LES *gets other cap pistol loaded with caps and brings rope, too. Returns shortly.*]

JIMMY

I'll use this part of the room for the fort.

LES

O.K. I'll have to sneak up on you. I found some lipstick on the dresser so I'm going to put that on as war paint. [*He smears all kinds of streaks on his face.*]

JIMMY

Why don't you get a knife, too? All Indians have knives to scalp people with.

LES

I haven't got a knife.

JIMMY

Get one out of the kitchen.

LES

I'm not supposed to play with knives. How about you?

JIMMY

So what. There's nobody here to tell on us.

LES

O.K. [*He goes for knife—returns with it. In his absence* JIMMY *arranges the furniture to set up a fortress.*]

JIMMY

I'm Rex Bitter—the good guy. [*Firing caps rapidly.*]

LES

[*Entering with war cries.*] Me Chief Mohawk. Here's my tomahawk and rope. Wah-wah-wah—me on warpath— after you Rex Bitter—wah-wah-wah.

JIMMY

[*Shooting caps.*] You can't get me. I got my trusty six-shooter. Take that and that.

[*Business of chasing and shooting to be worked out.*]

LES

[*Knocking* JIMMY *down.*] I got you. Youum my prisoner.

JIMMY

[*Getting up from floor—hands raised.*] O.K. But the Rangers will come and free me.

LES

Meum going to hangum youum.

JIMMY

The Rangers will save me.

LES

Now I got a rope and let's pretend you are standing ready to be hanged. Underneath there'll be a fire. Now you stand on this chair. Put the rope around your neck and

I'll pretend I'm going to cut the rope that hangs you.
Okay?

JIMMY

Got any matches? We can build a little fire in the waste-
paper basket. It's tin so-nothing will burn.

LES

There's some matches in the drawer there.

[JIMMY *gets some matches from table drawer.*]

JIMMY

[*Gets back on chair—rope looped around him.*] Hey, what
about the fire? [*Doorbell rings. It so surprises the boys that*
JIMMY *jumps off the chair as* LES *drops knife. . . .* JIMMY
runs to the door.]

[MRS. HERBERTSON *enters.*]

JIMMY

Oh, Mom!

MRS. HERBERTSON

It was getting late and . . . What's going on here?

LES

[*Frightened.*] We were just playing cowboys and Indians,
Mrs. Herbertson.

MRS. HERBERTSON

[*Surveying the rooms.*] Isn't anyone here with you boys?

JIMMY

No, ma'am.

MRS. HERBERTSON

Where's your mother and father?

LES

They went out to the Lodge and left Carol to stay with
me.

MRS. HERBERTSON
Carol—is she home? Where is she?

LES
She went out a little while ago.

JIMMY
She went to get us ice cream. [JIMMY *strikes a match.*]

MRS. HERBERTSON
What were you doing with this knife, and the rope—And Jimmy!—matches!

JIMMY
Chief Mohawk was going to hang me and scalp me when you knocked. [*Shoots pistol.*]

MRS. HERBERTSON
Dear God, what kind of a game is that? Don't you boys have any sense? You might have gotten killed and burned the place down. It's a miracle I came in on time.

LES
Yes, ma'am. But we weren't doing anything. It was just pretend stuff.

MRS. HERBERTSON
Well, you may look very innocent, my boy—— Oh, what's the use. We'd better get this room cleaned up, Lester. Help me get things in order. We'll stay with you until your parents return.

LES
Yes, ma'am.

[*The lights can start dimming as the cleaning up process goes on, going off right after* MRS. HERBERTSON *starts story. They move three chairs side by side in front of* X: A B C.]

MRS. HERBERTSON
I know what we'll do, I'll tell you a story.

JIMMY
About cowboys and Indians? [*Shoots pistol.*]

MRS. HERBERTSON
[*Grabbing pistol.*] No! I'll tell you about . . . about King Arthur and his knights. Now, let's see, how does it begin? Oh, yes . . . Well, now there was Merlin. He was a magician and he summoned all the gallant men together and there was going to be a tournament.

[*When she says "King Arthur," the boys let out audible sounds of boredom. Lights out. As the lights come back on, the room is as before. The boys are asleep and* MRS. HERBERTSON *is dozing in a chair. Off stage we can hear* BILL *and* SYLVIA *talking and laughing and turning the latch.*]

SYLVIA
[*Off stage.*] It was the most wonderful affair I've ever been to.

BILL
[*Off stage.*] And wasn't Cary the funniest thing you've seen in years? [*They laugh and enter into room.*]

MRS. HERBERTSON
[*Rising.*] It's about time you two got back here. I've never seen such irresponsible parents in all my life.

BILL
Mrs. Herbertson!

MRS. HERBERTSON
Don't Mrs. Herbertson me! If I hadn't come when I did, your son would have murdered my son. . . . And who knows, maybe your apartment would have been burned

down. . . . Maybe the whole house would have caught fire. . . . And maybe ten families would have lost their homes, their possessions, even their lives. . . . All if I hadn't come. . . . And all because you go out and have a good time and leave your child here alone. [*She wakes the boys.*]

SYLVIA
I don't understand, Mrs. Herbertson. Les—Les. Where's Carol, Les?

LES
Huh—she's gone.

JIMMY
She went out to get us ice cream.

BILL
How long has she been gone?

[LES *and* JIMMY *are yawning.*]

LES
I don't know. I've been sleeping.

MRS. HERBERTSON
She hasn't been here since eight forty-five. I've been here since then. I found them playing cowboys and Indians. . . . They had a noose . . . a real sharp knife . . . they even had matches to start a fire.

LES
I was just playing that I was going to hang and scalp Jimmy. He was Rex Bitter and I was Chief Mohawk.

[*During this part of the scene,* LES *and* JIMMY *whisper to each other, enjoying the excitement.*]

SYLVIA
I can't tell you how grateful we both are to you. I don't know how to thank you.

MRS. HERBERTSON

I don't want your thanks. I don't need them. Two of you
—and you can't take care of your boy decently. I'm a
working woman and alone—but I take care of my child.

BILL

Yes, Mrs. Herbertson. All we can say is we're sorry—and
we'll certainly get to the bottom of all this and find out
what happened.

MRS. HERBERTSON

I don't know what you can find out. Irresponsible, that's
what you are.

SYLVIA

Please, please, Mrs. Herbertson, let's not quarrel. We're
sorry. I can't think why Carol went out.

MRS. HERBERTSON

Carol—what's the use of talking to you if two grown
people would dream of leaving a little boy with a teenage
girl. Don't you read the papers? How can you trust a
modern adolescent?

BILL

We could always trust Carol. Something must have happened.

MRS. HERBERTSON

Sure something happened. That's pretty plain. All adolescents are reckless. But I don't expect you to care about
that. You're as bad as she.

SYLVIA

I suppose you are right—according to your understanding.

BILL

Look, Mrs. Herbertson. It's getting pretty late. Thanks for
all you've done. Let's get the boys to sleep. It's been a

pretty hectic night all around. Let me walk you to your apartment.

MRS. HERBERTSON
That's not necessary. I found my way here alone. I can find my way out. Come on, Jimmy. [*As they exit.*] But you haven't heard the last of this, I can tell you.

JIMMY
[*At door.*] Good night!

[MRS. HERBERTSON *and* JIMMY *exit* Z.]

BILL
Everything just seems to happen to us. Well, come on, Les. I'll turn on the light for you and you can go to bed.

LES
[*Rises.*] O.K. Good night, Mom.

SYLVIA
[*Putting the chairs in order as originally set up.*] Good night, Les dear.

BILL
I'll be right back.

LES
[*On exiting* X.] Pop, are you mad at us? Are you, Pop?

BILL
Nope. Now let's get ready for bed. [*Off stage.*] Hurry up and get ready and then call me when you're ready for me to come in and turn off the light.

LES
[*Off stage.*] O.K., Pop. Gee, I'm glad you're not mad at me.

BILL
[*Re-entering from* X.] Shall we wait up for Carol?

SYLVIA

[*Sitting at* c.] Yes. I'm a little confused about the whole thing. Carol has always been dependable. I can't see what made her just pick up and go out.

BILL

[*Sitting at* a.] It must have been something pretty damn important to her. It's just not like Carol.

SYLVIA

I just felt that I shouldn't have gone. I knew I should have stayed here with Les. If anything had happened to Les I'd never forgive myself. . . . I'd . . .

BILL

Now look here, Sylvia. You're just letting Mrs. Herbertson frighten you. Nothing happened to Les or to Jimmy, so just calm yourself. Everything's all right.

SYLVIA

What time is it now?

BILL

A quarter to one.

SYLVIA

I wonder if anything's happened to her. You know, she said something about coming back with ice cream for the children.

BILL

Let's wait up for a while. I'm sure she's O.K. Carol's been out later on dates. You've never worried before about her.

SYLVIA

Yes, but I always knew where she went. I don't have any idea where she is or what she's doing right now. Bill, do you think anything could have happened?

BILL

If anything did, I think Carol would have gotten in touch

with us. Let's just relax a little, and, well, Sylvia, I've been thinking a great deal about this problem. You know, our kids are growing up so fast and now they're under the impression that they have their own lives to live.

SYLVIA

Yes. I suppose so, Bill. Why, when we went out . . .

BILL

[*Laughing.*] Ha! Ha! Ha! . . . I was wondering if Mrs. Herbertson is noticing the change. Remember her saying something about modern adolescents?

LES

[*Off stage.*] Pop. You can turn off the light now.

[BILL *exits* X.]

SYLVIA

[*Calling to* LES.] Did you brush your teeth?

LES

[*Off stage.*] Sure.

SYLVIA

Well, good night, dear.

LES

[*Off stage.*] Good night.

BILL

[*Off stage.*] Good night, son. [BILL *re-enters.*]

SYLVIA

[*Walking toward window.*] I think there's a car downstairs now. . . . I can't tell who's getting out. . . .

BILL

[*Pacing a little.*] What are you going to say to her?

SYLVIA

[*Crossing to him.*] Well, first of all I'm going to find out why she left the children here alone and what was so important to drag her away from her duty.

BILL

[*Stepping in front of her, center stage.*] And?

SYLVIA

Well . . . aren't you going to do anything to her . . . say anything to her? . . . After all, she's your daughter, too.

BILL

I've been trying to think of something that I could say to her . . . or something I could do that would make her remember that she can't just shrug responsibility off her shoulders. . . . But, Sylvia . . . was Les her responsibility?

SYLVIA

He most certainly was. She agreed to stay here and she should have thought of us. Suppose something happened while she was gone. . . .

BILL

I still don't know what to say or what to do.

SYLVIA

William Donlevy, you've got to say something. You can't just let her get away with this.

BILL

Will scolding her help any? She'll be gone tomorrow and the whole incident will blow over anyway. Why use up energy?

SYLVIA

You mean you're just going to sit back and ignore the whole thing?

BILL

I'm asking you sensibly, Sylvia, what can we do? What

will make her realize that even though we're parents we like to go out every now and then, too. What can we do?

SYLVIA

It sounds like Carol coming down the hall now.

BILL

Well, dear. What do we do now?

SYLVIA

I don't know, Bill. But there must be something.

[CAROL *enters.*]

CAROL

[*In a world of ecstasy, flopping in* A.] Hello, everybody. Isn't it wonderful out? Have a nice time?

BILL

Yeah, just wonderful. [*A little sarcastically.*] And what happened to you? Weren't you staying with Les?

CAROL

Just let me explain. I was sitting home when the phone rang and Anne Hughes called and she needed a date for the All-American, Carl Ruthers, and, well . . . I had a wonderful time. . . . But you're not even interested.

SYLVIA

Carol, dear, we're glad you had a good time. I'm awfully tired, dear. Can you tell us about it tomorrow? [*Very pensively.*]

CAROL

[*Very downcast.*] Yeah! [*Exits quickly.*]

LES

[*Off stage.*] Hey, Carol?

CAROL

[*Off stage.*] Yes?

LES

[*Off stage.*] Did you bring me my chocolate ice cream cone?

SYLVIA

You know, Bill, I see what you mean. What can we do about the whole thing? [*Exits* x.]

MY CLIENT CURLEY

By Norman Corwin

From Thirteen by Norman Corwin. Copyright 1942 by Norman Corwin.
Reprinted by permission of Holt, Rinehart and Winston, Inc.

CAST

Announcer	Man
Agent	Woman
Fatso	Spokesman
Stinky	Conductor
Bidder	Musician
Child	A. P. Representative
Girl	Eleanor Roosevelt
Disney	Philatelist
First Lepidopterist	Police Announcer
Second Lepidopterist	Winchell
Third Lepidopterist	Find-Curleyite
Editorial Writer	Waiter
Defender	Shipper
Knell	

Voices of the following newspapers and magazines:
Times, Post, Brooklyn Eagle, World-Telegram, News,
Gráfico, Le Temps, *Shanghai paper,* Variety, Life

Ladies and gentlemen: In the following play, any similarity to caterpillars, living or dead, is purely coincidental.

[MUSIC: *Symphonic treatment of "Yes, Sir, That's My Baby" up and out, under . . .*]

AGENT

There are some things a man doesn't like to talk about because they're . . . [*Breaks off.*] Well, I'll just tell this story about my client Curley, and then I'll go back to the agent business and try to forget it. But if I should get a lump in my throat while I'm telling it, I hope you'll understand, because this whole thing was so recent I still feel pretty upset about it.

To make a long story short, I'm out walking one day in the suburbs where I live, when my attention is attracted by two kids sitting on the side of the road and one of them is playing a harmonica.

[*Harmonica in, well off mike, after "the side of the road."*]

They're bent over, watching something on the ground, and I, being curious, go over to see what it is.

[*Fade in harmonica, playing "Yes, Sir, That's My Baby."*]

AGENT

Hiya, boys, what you got there?

[*Harmonica stops abruptly.*]

FATSO
We got a trained caterpillar.

AGENT
What's trained about it?

STINKY
He dances.

AGENT
[*Laughing.*] I don't believe it.

STINKY
He sure does.

FATSO
[*The business brains.*] Give us a nickel and we'll show you.

AGENT
[*Good-naturedly.*] Oh, a racket, eh? All right, I'm a sucker.
Here's two nickels.

FATSO
Thanks, Mister. Okay, play, Stinky.

[*Harmonica begins tune.*]

AGENT
[*Fascinated. After a moment.*] Well, what do you know!
[*To* STINKY.] Now stop.

[*Harmonica out.*]

AGENT
I'll be darned! Stops right when you do.

FATSO
[*Proudly.*] Sure. That's the way Stinky trained him, didn't
ya, Stinky?

STINKY

Aw, it was nothin'.

AGENT

[*Still incredulous.*] Play some more, Stinky.

[*Harmonica starts and plays through briefly to finish.*]

AGENT

[*Laughing with delight.*] Lies right down when you're finished!

STINKY

Sure, he's talented, ain't he? [*To* CURLEY, *affectionately.*] Come on up on my finger, Curley. Th—a-at's a boy!

AGENT

Does Curley dance to any kind of music?

FATSO

Nope. Only "Yes, Sir, That's My Baby."

AGENT

You mean to tell me he dances to only *one* tune?

STINKY

That's right. I tried lots more, but I guess he only likes that one.

AGENT

Well, why is that, do you suppose?

STINKY

Feller I know says he got a real musical ear.

FATSO

I guess that's what those two branches are on his head, huh? Musical ears.

AGENT

No, that's his antennae.

STINKY

Antenna? [*Laughs.*] He ain't no radio set! [*Vastly amused by his own joke, he laughs again.*]

FATSO

[*Joins in laughter.*]

AGENT

Say!

FATSO

What?

AGENT

I wonder if he's got any snake blood in him? You know there are some snakes who dance.

FATSO

No kiddin'?

AGENT

Here, let me take your harmonica a minute.

STINKY

Okay. Sure.

AGENT

Curley may be related to one of them Asiatic snakes or something. Lemme play it a minute.

[*Harmonica plays "Hoochie Koochie" (danse de ventre).*]

AGENT

[*Stopping.*] Nope. Won't budge. I guess it's an American caterpillar, all right.

STINKY

Oh, sure.

AGENT
[*All business.*] Look, fellers, I'll make you a proposition. How would you like to sell Curley?

FATSO
[*The commercial-minded.*] How much?

STINKY
[*The sustaining-minded.*] Wait a minute. I own Curley, and I don't wanna sell him.

AGENT
Why not, Stinky?

STINKY
[*Ashamed to confess he loves the thing.*] Well, because I— well—just *because!*

FATSO
[*Interpreting.*] Know why he don't wanna sell?

AGENT
Why?

FATSO
On account of he's stuck on him.

STINKY
Aw, shut up, Fatso!

AGENT
You mean you like Curley so much you don't want to part with him?

STINKY
I just don't want to sell him, that's all. Not even for a dollar. [*Afterthought.*] Not even for two dollars!

AGENT
Well, of course I don't think anybody'd ever offer you *that* much money.

S T I N K Y

I don't care. He's my pet, and I want to keep him. I trained him from a pup.

A G E N T

Now look, kiddo, I think you're a very bright and sensitive boy, and because of that, I'm going to make you an immediate cash payment of *five dollars* for Curley!

F A T S O

Hey! *Five bucks!* Holy smackerels! Whadda ya say, Stinky? Huh?

S T I N K Y

[*Almost in tears.*] Well—gosh—I dunno.

F A T S O

Take it, I'm tellin' ya! Now you can buy a bike!

S T I N K Y

[*Deserted by* FATSO *and now a martyr to his affection for Curley.*] Well, that sure is a lot of money—but, y'see—I *like* Curley, and I guess Curley likes me, too; and when we're alone I talk to him, and he understands me. [*Warming up; finding reasons to support his refusal to sell.*] Curley likes me around. He's very intelligent, even though he don't look so smart.

A G E N T

Oh, he looks smart, all right.

S T I N K Y

[*Deadly serious.*] You know—if somebody took him away from me—Curley would die.

A G E N T

Think so?

S T I N K Y

Sure. He's only human, ain't he? He would absolutely die.

AGENT

Listen to me, Stinky. I'm going to talk to you man to man. This caterpillar you've got is very valuable. He's worth a lot of money—'way more than five dollars, maybe.

FATSO

No kiddin'?

AGENT

Now this is what we're gonna do. Stinky, you're gonna *stay* with Curley and I'm gonna manage both of you. Curley will be my client!

FATSO

What's that mean?

STINKY

What's a client?

AGENT

Well, you wouldn't understand very well. That's something I'll have to explain to your parents, because I've got to get their signatures on a long-term contract with options. You're a minor under the law, you see.

STINKY

[*Apprehensive of the terminology.*] I didn't do anything wrong, did I?

[MUSIC: *Transitional cue, orchestra with harmonica.*]

AGENT

That was how it began. I get Curley under my management, and take him and Stinky with me. The first thing I do is start out after some publicity, and *say*—do those reporters eat it up! Front page, with pictures! Pictures of Curley and pictures of Stinky and pictures of me; pictures of my client dancing on a leaf, curling around the mayor's finger, climbing up a pretty model's leg, sitting in a tiny

box at the opera. And *headlines!* Headlines, like in the
Times . . .

TIMES
Swing Caterpillar Sways to Strains of "Yes, Sir, That's
My Baby"; Fred Astaire of Insect World Demonstrates
Almost Human Sense of Rhythm.

[MUSIC: *Motif.*]

AGENT
The *Post* . . .

POST
Curley in Custody of Stinky, Young Svengali of Caterpillars.

[MUSIC: *Motif.*]

AGENT
The *Brooklyn Eagle* . . .

BROOKLYN EAGLE
Insect Phenomenon Learned to Truck in Truck Garden,
Manager Avers.

[MUSIC: *Motif.*]

AGENT
The *World-Telegram* . . .

WORLD-TELEGRAM
The Curley Crawl Becomes New National Dance Sensa-
tion.

[MUSIC: *Motif.*]

AGENT
The *Daily News* . . .

NEWS
BUG CUTS RUG! Story on page 2.

[MUSIC: *Finale treatment of motif.*]

AGENT

And sure enough, with all that publicity, things really begin to happen. First, Bill Robinson introduces the Curley Capers at the Cotton Club!

[MUSIC: *Effect of solo tap dancing.*]

AGENT

Then Raymond Scott writes a song called "The Caterpillar Creep."

[MUSIC: *"Caterpillar Creep."*]

AGENT

Then half a dozen agencies bid for the rights to syndicate a comic strip.

BIDDER

Four hundred twenty-nine papers, five days a week, making a grand total of . . .

AGENT

Other companies pay me royalties for Curley balloons and spaghetti and dolls and toys and picturebooks and decorations on the outside of drinking glasses.

CHILD

[*Whining.*] Maw, buy me the glass with Curley's picture on it!

AGENT

And to make a long story short, I get a vaudeville offer; the money begins to roll in; I hire an expensive suite and a secretary . . .

GIRL

Curley Enterprises! Good afternoon!

AGENT
I buy Stinky a bike and a new suit of clothes.

STINKY
Gee, thanks!

AGENT
The publicity begins to pile up, and at the height of the excitement, I get a wire from Hollywood!

DISNEY
[*On filter.*] Offer ten thousand for Curley appearance in feature-length cartoon. Propose using live character for first time among cartoon characters. Appreciate immediate answer. Would like to rush story and production. Cordially, Walt Disney.

AGENT
Mm. Oh—er—Miss Neilson!

GIRL
Yes?

AGENT
Take a wire to Walt Disney, Hollywood, California.

GIRL
Yes, sir.

AGENT
Curley price one hundred thousand.

GIRL
Is that all?

AGENT
Do you think I should ask for more?

GIRL
No, I mean is there any more to the wire?

[*Phone rings. Receiver off.*]

GIRL

Curley Enterprises. . . . Just a moment, please. [*To* AGENT.] *Time Magazine* on the line. Will you take it on the table phone?

AGENT

[*Going off.*] All right.

[*Sound of phone receiver off, and following conversation is background all the way through to end of scene.*]

AGENT

Hello? Yes? This is him. . . . Yes. . . . Well, you see . . . yuh. . . . Uhuh. . . . No, I discovered him in the boy's possession. . . . That's right. . . .

[*Second phone rings; perspective with the* GIRL.]

GIRL

Curley Enterprises. . . . Well, he's busy on another line. Who? . . . Oh yes. He wanted me to tell you to order a special air-mail daily shipment of willow leaves from Florida. [*Third phone rings.*] Wait a minute, will you? [*Fourth phone rings; alternates with third. Finally the flustered* GIRL *can stand it no longer, and she shouts to the* AGENT.] You better hire some more secretaries!

No. . . . No. . . . Yes, sure. . . . No, he hasn't yet. . . . Right. . . . I keep him right here. . . . Stinky looks after him most of the time. . . . Yes. . . . What? . . . No. . . . Oh, no. . . . I beg your pardon. . . . Oh, by all means. . . . From the very first, yes . . . that's right . . . that's right. . . . Hm? . . . Not yet. Probably not for another week or two. . . . Absolutely. . . . Well, we tried all kinds of tunes . . . no, sir . . . which . . . which . . . are you referring to? . . . No. . . . I don't. . . . Hm? . . . Yes. . . .

[MUSIC: *Sock cue. Rides over ringing phones and conversation.*]

AGENT

Well, things are going in great shape and Curley is making us a bundle of dough, when all of a sudden I get three visitors I didn't figure on.

FIRST LEPIDOPTERIST

We have been reading about your wonderful specimen in the papers, and we have come to ask permission to examine it.

AGENT

Examine it? What for?

SECOND LEPIDOPTERIST

We are lepidopterists.

AGENT

Lepidopterists? But Curley's a caterpillar, not a leopard.

THIRD LEPIDOPTERIST

Ah no, my dear man—lepidopterology is a branch of entomology dealing with the insect order of which your—er—shall we say client—is a member.

AGENT

Well, I'm sure Curley doesn't want to be examined by nobody.

FIRST LEPIDOPTERIST

Oh, come, come! If this caterpillar is as remarkable as the newspapers say, then you certainly owe science the courtesy of permitting an examination.

SECOND LEPIDOPTERIST

Exactly.

THIRD LEPIDOPTERIST
It would be nothing short of criminal to withhold such knowledge from science.

AGENT
[*Grudgingly.*] Well—if you want to put it that way, I suppose——

FIRST LEPIDOPTERIST
It will take no more than two minutes.

AGENT
Oh—I suppose it's all right. Come with me, please.

[*Steps, as of group passing from one room to another. Door opens, closes.*]

AGENT
Hello, Stinky.

STINKY
Hello.

AGENT
This is Master Stinky, gentlemen—discoverer and trainer of my client. He guards Curley all the time.

ALL
[*Ad lib greetings.*]

AGENT
Well, there he is in that box. Please be careful how you handle him.

SECOND LEPIDOPTERIST
Aaahhh—here you are!

THIRD LEPIDOPTERIST
My! Muscular little fellow, isn't he?

FIRST LEPIDOPTERIST

Mm-hm. [*Examining.*] Normal mandible . . . unusually conspicuous first maxillae . . .

SECOND LEPIDOPTERIST

I say, watch out there, Doctor, he's trying to bite you!

THIRD LEPIDOPTERIST

Ha! Never been attacked by a caterpillar before! Astounding!

FIRST LEPIDOPTERIST

See here, Doctor—just notice this remarkable elongation of the abdominal feet.

SECOND LEPIDOPTERIST

Yes, quite. And doesn't this feature make you think of the *Aglais antiopa?*

THIRD LEPIDOPTERIST

Incredible!

FIRST LEPIDOPTERIST

Look here! Isn't *this* remarkable! I've never seen such ocelli except in the *Melanargia galathea.* And the chitinization . . . !

AGENT

No kidding?

SECOND LEPIDOPTERIST

[*To the* AGENT.] Well, sir! Congratulations! This is a remarkable specimen, even before we test its reactions to musical stimuli.

AGENT

Gosh, thanks.

THIRD LEPIDOPTERIST

It is of the ordinary genus *Papilio rutulus,* mind you, but it has the most extraordinary features. . . .

AGENT

Thanks very much.

FIRST LEPIDOPTERIST

But—ahum—we feel that the specimen would be much more valuable to society if you, instead of exhibiting it for commercial purposes, were to—uh—lend or donate it to the Museum of Natural History, where it could be further studied by the leading entomologists of the world.

AGENT

But I . . .

SECOND LEPIDOPTERIST

Yes, and when it dies, we can dissect it, and . . .

STINKY

[*Terrified by the thought.*] No! No! They're not gonna take him away! [*Crying.*] Don't let them take Curley! [*Keeps protesting and crying under.*]

THIRD LEPIDOPTERIST

Don't cry, my boy, we're not going to hurt him.

FIRST LEPIDOPTERIST

[*Ignoring the commotion.*] An insect like this occurs probably once in a million years—and surely, for the sake of a few dollars, you're not going to risk injuring him by overwork!

AGENT

[*Rising above mercenary motives.*] Are you accusing me of sacrificing Curley's health for *profits?* [*Scornfully.*] Why, that's ridiculous! Curley is . . .

[*Knocking on door. All noise stops, including* STINKY'S *protestation.*]

AGENT

Yes—come in.

[*Door opens.*]

GIRL

Just got another wire from the coast! Disney's raised his offer to twenty thousand!

AGENT

[*Heatedly.*] Twenty! Tell him a hundred thousand or nothing!

[MUSIC: *Sock cue up, then down behind.* . . .]

AGENT

Well, the papers get hold of the lepidopterists' story, and there's another pile of publicity. It gets to be a moral issue, with preachers delivering sermons, and all like that. I'm attacked editorially for exploiting caterpillar labor.

EDITORIAL

[*Fade on.*] . . . of the shameless exploitation of a little unsuspecting insect, by a mercenary agent who has turned to his own greedy personal advantage a natural phenomenon which belongs nowhere else but in a museum. The public at large is to be condemned for encouraging this veritable slave-trader to continue . . . [*Fading.*] . . . his career of rank exhibitionism, unabashed and in the full glare of wide publicity . . .

AGENT

But on the other hand, I am defended as an individualist who refuses to submit to regimentation!

DEFENDER

A man owns a clever bug. He has the right to manage that bug. There is no *question* about his status as manager of that bug. Yet he is asked to release his client for scientific purposes. He refuses. He has a right to refuse. Nobody denies that right. Yet in certain quarters he is attacked merely because he insists upon his constitutional guarantees. We say it is consoling to find a man, in this day of reckless encroachment upon the individual, who will stand up and fight for his rights. We wish him well. We stand behind him, foursquare, our feet firmly implanted in the soil from which his bug has sprung, to support his defiance . . . [*Fading.*] . . . of those who would turn back the progress . . .

AGENT

The American Legion and the Daughters of the American Revolution send Curley an engraved silver-plated twig and a miniature flag to put on top of his box. The foreign correspondents get busy and cable stories to their papers. In Madrid, the Spanish *Gráfico* comes out with a dirty dig.

GRÁFICO

Más los norteamericanos no deben olvidar que la danza española es la mejor de todas y que si la oruga del Señor Stinky tuviese un poquitin de buen oído para la música, reconocería los irresistibles ritmos de la jota, y no se limitaría a tocar "Yes, Sir, That's My Baby." Es un insulto a los países latinos que este insecto . . .

AGENT

How do you like that for nerve? That's the Latin mind for ya! But darned if the Curley motif ain't reflected, as they say, in the latest Paris fashions. Caterpillar doodads on hats and coats and scarfs and all like that. *Le Temps*— that's a newspaper in Paris—comes out with a plug.

LE TEMPS

Tous ceux qui aiment la nature, de même que ceux qui s'intéressent aux aspects les plus subtiles de la danse et de la musique, se réjouiront avec notre république sœur, les Etats-Unis, de la découverte faite récemment par un garçon qui s'appelle Stinky . . . la découverte d'une chenille dansante que le monde connaît affectueusement sous le nom de Curley. Et c'est remarquable de constater

*que cet insecte ne consent á danser que si l'on joue l'air
justement célèbre: "Oui, monsieur, C'est Mon Bébé"!*

AGENT
And you know what? My clipping service sends me some
encouraging comment from Shanghai, which I get my
laundryman to translate.

CHINESE

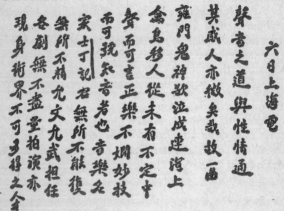

AGENT
The Maharajah of Lahore sends Curley some willow
leaves from the sacred willow trees of the temple.

STINKY
Gee, look, a package from a place named Lakeshore with
a lot of funny-looking stamps.

AGENT
Lahore, not Lakeshore.

STINKY
C'n I have the stamps?

AGENT
Yeah—here y'are. . . . I sign Curley up for a superspecial
movie short, and it sweeps the box office of the country in
spite of terrible weather, including blizzards and rain-
storms. *Variety* reports:

VARIETY
Bliz and Driz Fail to Fizzle Biz as Bug Biffs B.O. from
N.Y. to L.A.

AGENT
Life Magazine runs a Margaret Bourke-White picture of
Curley on the cover, with the caption:

LIFE
Curley.

AGENT
CBS does a pickup direct from Curley's box, bringing the
sound of Curley eating dinner.

KNELL
This is Jack Knell speaking to you from the headquarters
of Curley Enterprises, where we have a microphone buried
among willow leaves, to pick up the sound of the world's
leading insect dancer, busy . . . [*Fading.*] . . . eating
dinner after a hard day's work of exhibiting his talents
to the press. . . .

AGENT
The *New Yorker* comes out with a cartoon showing
Martha Graham nibbling willow leaves.

MAN
[*Laughing.*] Did you see this cartoon in the *New Yorker?*

WOMAN
Lemme see. [*Silence.*] Well, what's funny about that?

MAN
For heaven's sake, don't you get the point?

WOMAN
No.

MAN
Well, don't you know who Martha Graham is?

WOMAN
Yes.

MAN
And you know who Curley is, of course?

WOMAN
The caterpillar.

MAN
Yes. . . . Well, now . . . [*Fading.*] . . . you see, Curley lives on willow leaves, and . . .

AGENT
Walt Disney raises his bid to fifty thousand, but I still hold out for a hundred thousand; Grover Whalen invites Curley to do an English country dance on the cover of the Magna Carta at the World's Fair; and, to make a long story short, everything's going along hunky-dory until one day *more* public-spirited guys get ahold of Curley—only this time they're not scientists, but musicians.

SPOKESMAN
[*Fading on.*] And therefore, in the interests of music, we of the committee feel that you would be rendering an invaluable service to musical knowledge if you would permit us to test the effect of *classical* music on your client.

AGENT
But what good will that do anybody?

SPOKESMAN

Why, it may open up an entirely new field of psychology in relation to music. The world knows very little about musical instincts of animals, and nothing at all about insects'. Now . . .

AGENT

But you're wasting your time. Curley dances to only one tune.

SPOKESMAN

Have you *tried* other tunes?

AGENT

Why, sure. Tell him what you've played, Stinky.

STINKY

I played "It Ain't Gonna Rain No More," "My Country, 'Tis of Thee," "The Beer Barrel Polka," "Shine On, Harvest Moon," "The Music Goes Round and . . ."

SPOKESMAN

Ah, but no *classical* music!

AGENT

Sure we did. I myself played "Ah, Sweet Mystery of Life," by Victor Herbert.

SPOKESMAN

[*Condescendingly.*] But you haven't tried any symphonies, have you?

AGENT

[*Straight.*] Disney's trying to get us for a Silly Symphony right now. His latest offer . . .

SPOKESMAN

No, I'm afraid you don't understand. Let me explain what we propose to do. [*Fading.*] We get Curley in a studio with an orchestra and go through a careful series of tests, using selected symphonic music of dancelike tempo. Now, by the choice of representative works, we can quickly establish . . .

[*Rap of baton.*]

CONDUCTOR

All right! I know you're tired, gentlemen; we've now been through sixty-seven pieces already. But let's try a few more, and then we'll quit until tomorrow.

MUSICIAN

Has the caterpillar moved at all?

CONDUCTOR

So far he hasn't budged once, but maybe we'll get him with the "Habañera" from *Carmen*.

[*Baton rapping for attention.* MUSIC: *"Habañera" for about twelve measures. Then.*]

CONDUCTOR

[*Perfunctorily; this is the sixty-eighth time he's had to stop almost at the beginning.*] Stop . . . stop.

[MUSIC: *Out.*]

CONDUCTOR

All right, try Number 69—*Rosamunde* ballet.

[MUSIC: *Same business as before.*]

CONDUCTOR

Stop.

[MUSIC: *Out.*]

CONDUCTOR

Next, Number 70—Strauss's "Perpetuum Mobile."

[MUSIC: *Same business as before. Fade under.*]

AGENT

For two and a half days this went on, and finally, after the two-hundred-second try, something happened that really made the papers sit up and take notice all over again. The Associated Press next day carried this story.

[*Fade in news printer. Establish, and take down for.*]

ASSOCIATED PRESS

Curley, the terpsichorean caterpillar, today staggered scientists and musicians when he suddenly went into a stately dance upon hearing the second movement of Beethoven's *Eighth Symphony*. The movement, marked "Allegretto Scherzando," was the two-hundred-third musical sampling performed in an effort to determine whether the super-caterpillar could, or would, dance to anything besides the song "Yes, Sir, That's My Baby." The insect further astonished observers by dancing in a contrapuntal manner to an arrangement of melodies from both the song and the movement.

Scientists are unable to explain the phenomenon. [*Fade in "Allegretto Scherzando" movement after "unable."*] The management of the caterpillar announced meanwhile that Curley will appear as the lead in a ballet entitled "Extravaganza for Insects Only" by William Saroyan, and that Curley will also be seen soon in a dance recital at Carnegie Hall.

[MUSIC: *Up full and down, under.*]

AGENT

Well, then things really begin to break for us. Mrs. Roosevelt writes about it in her column, "My Day."

ELEANOR

It is not often that a creature smaller than one's little finger can completely captivate the imagination of millions. Yet such is the remarkable truth about the caterpillar named

Curley, and only today I was telling the President that
. . . [*Fading.*] . . . it has been many years since the
country has become so interested in . . .

AGENT

There's talk among stamp collectors of issuing a special
Curley stamp.

PHILATELIST

And since the Curley stamp would be the only insect
subject in existence, its value to philately would naturally
. . . [*Fading.*] . . . assume prodigious proportions . . .

AGENT

Scientific societies offer to investigate Curley's genius—
and would you believe that the annual convention of the
American Lepidopterological and Entomological Academy even invites Stinky to lecture before it.

STINKY

[*Echo—hesitantly; scared; obviously no speechmaker.*] Er
—so I says to my mother, "Ma, can I have a penny? I want
to buy a piece of candy," so my mother says yes, so she gives
me the penny—er—so on my way to the store, I see a caterpillar—uh—crossing the road—er—um—so I stopped to
watch it, see? So then [*Fading.*] I picked it up, and then I
started to whistle a song—uh—and it happened to be—er
—"Yes, Sir, That's My Baby."

AGENT

And all this time the money keeps coming in. We're getting along fine, although it costs a lot to keep up my expensive offices and staff of secretaries, but I'm figuring on
getting the big dough—the hundred thousand from Disney, and then retiring, see? Well, to make a long story
short, there are a couple of exchanges of telegrams and
phone calls, with me holding out for my price, and then
one night Disney wires.

DISNEY

[*Filter.*] Will meet your price of hundred thousand. Please fly out with Curley next plane.

AGENT

Wow! Am I excited! I rush into the next room, where Stinky and Curley are sleeping.

[*Door.*]

AGENT

Stinky! Wake up! We're rich! We're practically millionaires!

STINKY

[*Sleepily.*] What's the matter?

AGENT

[*Excitedly.*] Come on, kid! Get your clothes on! Hurry! You're gonna take a long airplane ride with me and Curley! And, boy, I'm gonna buy Curley the juiciest willow leaf he ever ate in his life! . . . Now lemme tell the news to Curley. [*As if opening Curley's box.*] Here you are, little fella, here you . . . [*Freezes, then panicky.*] Where is he? Why isn't he in his box? Where's Curley? *Curley!*

STINKY

[*Refusing to believe.*] I put him to bed all right. Ain't he in his box?

AGENT

Quick! Look all around the room. Under the carpet, under the bed, on the walls—everywhere—And be careful where you walk!

STINKY

[*Half calling, half crying.*] Curley! Come back! Curley! Where are you, Curley?

AGENT

Curley! Curley, listen . . . [*Sings "Yes, Sir," in a croaking, terror-stricken voice.*]

STINKY

[*Joins in the general desultory singing, interspersed with cries for Curley.*]

AGENT

Curley! I love you! Where are you?

STINKY

Curley, don't leave us!

AGENT

A hundred thousand bucks, Curley! [*Sings vehemently; breaks off when he gets an idea.*] Here, Stinky! Take this flashlight and look for him along the corridor and ask the manager to let you look at the bottom of the elevator shaft. Meanwhile I'll phone the police!

STINKY

[*Goes off half singing, half crying.*]

[*Phone receiver jiggles.*]

AGENT

Operator! Operator! Get me the police headquarters! Operator!

[*Siren.*]

POLICE RADIO

[*Filter.*] Calling all cars. Calling all cars. Be on the lookout for a dancing caterpillar. Be on the lookout for a dancing caterpillar. C-A—T-E—R-P-I—L-L—A-R—caterpillar. That is all!

[*Code.*]

WINCHELL

Flash! The Federal Bureau of Investigation will neither deny nor confirm rumors that Curley, the hundred-thousand-dollar caterpillar, was *kidnaped!*

[*Single Chime.*]

ANNOUNCER

Ladies and gentlemen, we have been requested by the civic authorities to make the following announcement. Whenever you hear the song "Yes, Sir, That's My Baby" will you please watch very carefully, wherever you may be, for a dancing caterpillar in your vicinity. This announcement is [*Fading.*] in reference to Curley, the famous caterpillar whose recent career has . . .

AGENT

The whole country searches in vain; nobody's seen Curley. The police throw out a dragnet. Posses are formed. Radio stations play "Yes, Sir, That's My Baby" at intervals throughout the day, and ask all listeners to be on the look-out; Curley fans from all over send in money for a Find-Curley Fund.

FIND-CURLEYITE

[*Orating—slight echo.*] And I am privileged, as president of the Find-Curley Club, to announce to the members that the Find-Curley Fund has reached the impressive and staggering total of twelve thousand, three hundred eighty-five dollars and fourteen cents, with the entire South yet to be heard from!

CAST

[*Great applause.*]

FIND-CURLEYITE

And I am positive that every mother's son of you—yes, and every father's daughter—will pledge his or her heart and hand to the one main and permanent objective—that Curley may be found!

CAST
[*Even greater applause.*]

AGENT
But nobody finds Curley. And now that he's gone, I begin to realize how much I love that bug. I begin to understand why it was Stinky couldn't bear to sell him to me, 'way back in those happy days. I can't bear thinking of willow leaves. I find myself hating all birds and looking suspiciously at cats. And I take to drinking. . . .

[*Light background of sound.*]

WAITER
What will it be for you, sir?

AGENT
A triple zombie.

WAITER
Are you sure you . . .

AGENT
A triple zombie!

WAITER
Yes, sir. . . .

[*Background sound out.*]

AGENT
And even Stinky tries to drink his way out of his grief. . . .

[*Background sound in.*]

WAITER
And what will it be for you, young man?

STINKY
A cup of coffee—and make it *black!*

WAITER
Are you sure you want . . .

STINKY
Black coffee!

WAITER
Yes, sir.

[*Background sound out.*]

AGENT
Meanwhile, sympathizers from all over the world, including Scandinavian countries, send me caterpillars, hoping maybe they have found Curley and are eligible for a reward offered by the Find-Curley Fund!

SHIPPER
Mister, here's another barrel of caterpillars from Australia. Where shall I put it?

AGENT
Give it to the zoo.

SHIPPER
Which zoo, mister?

AGENT
Any zoo, any zoo—so long as you get it out of here!

SHIPPER
Okay, mister.

[*Door closes.*]

AGENT
Days go by. Weeks go by. I send Stinky home.

STINKY
[*Tearfully.*] Good-by.

AGENT
Good-by Stinky. Well, at least you got a nice suit of clothes on you, and a fine automobile and a chauffeur to drive you home.

STINKY
I would rather have Curley back again.

AGENT
Yes, I know. Well—good-by.

STINKY
G'by.

AGENT
G'by.

STINKY
G'by. [*Pause.*]

AGENT
And then one day I'm sitting in my place, playing sadly on the piano with one finger, as is my want.

[MUSIC: *One-finger plunking of "Yes, Sir" on piano.*]

AGENT
All of a sudden, out from under the music rack creeps— Curley!

[MUSIC: *Piano stops.*]

AGENT
Only he's changed. He's different. He's not dancing any more. He—he's a—*a butterfly!*

[MUSIC: *Orchestra sneaks in with Beethoven movement softly.*]

AGENT
[*To* CURLEY, *tenderly.*] Curley! Hello, Curley . . . you're a big boy now, ain't you? . . . [*Low, narrating.*] He flutters his wings a little when I say that, and I stroke his antennae, which are now very long and beautiful. I see he's getting restless for the outdoors, where he no doubt hears the call of his mate, so I sing a farewell to him.

[MUSIC: *Orchestra stops.*]

AGENT

[*Sings softly "Yes, Sir."*] He flutters around my head, and then flies over to a picture of Stinky on the bureau, and then flutters back to me . . . and after one long look at me, he flies out of the window, never more to come back again.

[MUSIC: *Sneak in slow reprise combining both the Beethoven and "Yes, Sir" themes, and hold under.*]

AGENT

To make a long story short, I sit down, and I feel like crying. In fact, I do cry. [*Pause.*] Yes, who would ever think that a grown man would ever cry about a caterpillar? But I did, and I'm not ashamed to admit it.

[MUSIC: *Up briefly, then down again for.*]

AGENT

Well . . . that's the story of my client Curley.

[MUSIC: *Up to finish.*]

VISIT TO A SMALL PLANET

By Gore Vidal

From Visit to a Small Planet and Other Television Plays, *by Gore Vidal.*
Copyright © 1956 *by Gore Vidal. Reprinted by permission of Little, Brown
and Co.*

CAST

Kreton
Roger Spelding
Ellen Spelding
Mrs. Spelding
Two Technicians
John Randolph
General Powers
Aide
Paul Laurent
Second Visitor
President of Paraguay

ACT ONE

Stock Shot: The night sky, stars. Then slowly a luminous object arcs into view. As it is almost upon us, dissolve to the living room of the Spelding house in Maryland.

  Superimpose card: "The Time: The Day After To-morrow"

  The room is comfortably balanced between the expensively decorated and the homely. ROGER SPELDING *is concluding his TV broadcast. He is middle-aged, unctuous, resonant. His wife, bored and vague, knits passively while he talks at his desk. Two technicians are on hand, operating the equipment. His daughter,* ELLEN, *a lively girl of twenty, fidgets as she listens.*

SPELDING
[*Into microphone.*] . . . and so, according to General Powers . . . who should know if anyone does . . . the flying object which has given rise to so much irresponsible conjecture is nothing more than a meteor passing through the earth's orbit. It is not, as many believe, a secret weapon of this country. Nor is it a space ship as certain lunatic elements have suggested. General Powers has assured me that it is highly doubtful there is any form of life on other planets capable of building a space ship. "If any traveling is to be done in space, we will do it first." And those are his exact words. . . . Which winds up another week of news. [*Crosses to pose with wife and daughter.*] This is Roger Spelding, saying good night to Mother and Father America, from my old homestead in Silver Glen, Maryland, close to the warm pulse-beat of the nation.

TECHNICIAN
Good show tonight, Mr. Spelding.

SPELDING
Thank you.

TECHNICIAN
Yes sir, you were right on time.

[SPELDING *nods wearily, his mechanical smile and heartiness suddenly gone.*]

MRS. SPELDING
Very nice, dear. Very nice.

TECHNICIAN
See you next week, Mr. Spelding.

SPELDING
Thank you, boys.

[*Technicians go.*]

SPELDING
Did you like the broadcast, Ellen?

ELLEN
Of course I did, Daddy.

SPELDING
Then what did I say?

ELLEN
Oh, that's not fair.

SPELDING
It's not very flattering when one's own daughter won't listen to what one says while millions of people . . .

ELLEN
I always listen, Daddy, you know that.

MRS. SPELDING

We love your broadcasts, dear. I don't know what we'd do without them.

SPELDING

Starve.

ELLEN

I wonder what's keeping John?

SPELDING

Certainly not work.

ELLEN

Oh, Daddy, stop it! John works very hard and you know it.

MRS. SPELDING

Yes, he's a perfectly nice boy, Roger. I like him.

SPELDING

I know. I know: he has every virtue except the most important one: he has no get-up-and-go.

ELLEN

[*Precisely.*] He doesn't want to get up and he doesn't want to go because he's already where he wants to be on his own farm which is exactly where *I'm* going to be when we're married.

SPELDING

More thankless than a serpent's tooth is an ungrateful child.

ELLEN

I don't think that's right. Isn't it "more deadly . . ."

SPELDING

Whatever the exact quotation is, I stand by the sentiment.

MRS. SPELDING

Please don't quarrel. It always gives me a headache.

SPELDING

I never quarrel. I merely reason, in my simple way, with Miss Know-it-all here.

ELLEN

Oh, Daddy! Next you'll tell me I should marry for money.

SPELDING

There is nothing wrong with marrying a wealthy man. The horror of it has always eluded me. However, my only wish is that you marry someone hard-working, ambitious, a man who'll make his mark in the world. Not a boy who plans to sit on a farm all his life, growing peanuts.

ELLEN

English walnuts.

SPELDING

Will you stop correcting me?

ELLEN

But, Daddy, John grows walnuts . . .

[JOHN *enters, breathlessly.*]

JOHN

Come out! Quickly. It's coming this way. It's going to land right here!

SPELDING

What's going to land?

JOHN

The space ship. Look!

SPELDING

Apparently you didn't hear my broadcast. The flying object in question is a meteor, not a space ship.

[JOHN *has gone out with* ELLEN. SPELDING *and* MRS. SPELDING *follow.*]

MRS. SPELDING

Oh, my! Look! Something *is* falling! Roger, you don't think it's going to hit the house, do you?

SPELDING

The odds against being hit by a falling object that size are, I should say, roughly, ten million to one.

JOHN

Ten million to one or not it's going to land right here and it's *not* falling.

SPELDING

I'm sure it's a meteor.

MRS. SPELDING

Shouldn't we go down to the cellar?

SPELDING

If it's not a meteor, it's an optical illusion . . . mass hysteria.

ELLEN

Daddy, it's a real space ship. I'm sure it is.

SPELDING

Or maybe a weather balloon. Yes, that's what it is. General Powers said only yesterday . . .

JOHN

It's landing!

SPELDING

I'm going to call the police . . . the army! [*Bolts inside.*]

ELLEN

Oh look how it shines!

JOHN

Here it comes!

MRS. SPELDING
Right in my rose garden!

ELLEN
Maybe it's a balloon.

JOHN
No, it's a space ship and right in your own backyard.

ELLEN
What makes it shine so?

JOHN
I don't know but I'm going to find out. [*Runs off toward the light.*]

ELLEN
Oh, darling, don't! John, please! John, John come back!

[SPELDING, *wide-eyed, returns.*]

MRS. SPELDING
Roger, it's landed right in my rose garden.

SPELDING
I got General Powers. He's coming over. He said they've been watching this thing. They . . . they don't know what it is.

ELLEN
You mean it's nothing of ours?

SPELDING
They believe it . . . [*Swallows hard.*] . . . it's from outer space.

ELLEN
And John's down there! Daddy, get a gun or something.

SPELDING
Perhaps we'd better leave the house until the army gets here.

ELLEN
We can't leave John.

SPELDING
I can. [*Peers nearsightedly.*] Why, it's not much larger than a car. I'm sure it's some kind of meteor.

ELLEN
Meteors are blazing hot.

SPELDING
This is a cold one . . .

ELLEN
It's opening . . . the whole side's opening! [*Shouts.*] John! Come back! Quick. . . .

MRS. SPELDING
Why, there's a man getting out of it! [*Sighs.*] I feel much better already. I'm sure if we ask him, he'll move that thing for us. Roger, you ask him.

SPELDING
[*Ominously.*] If it's really a man?

ELLEN
John's shaking hands with him. [*Calls.*] John darling, come on up here . . .

MRS. SPELDING
And bring your friend . . .

SPELDING
There's something wrong with the way that creature looks . . . if it is a man and not a . . . not a monster.

MRS. SPELDING
He looks perfectly nice to me.

[JOHN *and the* VISITOR *appear. The* VISITOR *is in his forties, a mild, pleasant-looking man with side-whiskers*

*and dressed in the fashion of 1860. He pauses when he
sees the three people, in silence for a moment. They
stare back at him, equally interested.*]

VISITOR

I seem to've made a mistake. I *am* sorry. I'd better go back
and start over again.

SPELDING

My dear sir, you've only just arrived. Come in, come in.
I don't need to tell you what a pleasure this is . . . Mister
. . . Mister . . .

VISITOR

Kreton . . . This *is* the wrong costume, isn't it?

SPELDING

Wrong for what?

KRETON

For the country, and the time.

SPELDING

Well, it's a trifle old-fashioned.

MRS. SPELDING

But really awfully handsome.

KRETON

Thank you.

MRS. SPELDING

[*To husband.*] Ask him about moving that thing off my
rose bed.

[SPELDING *leads them all into living room.*]

SPELDING

Come on in and sit down. You must be tired after your
trip.

KRETON
Yes, I am a little. [*Looks around delightedly.*] Oh, it's better than I'd hoped!

SPELDING
Better? What's better?

KRETON
The house . . . that's what you call it? Or is this an apartment?

SPELDING
This is a house in the State of Maryland, U.S.A.

KRETON
In the late 20th century! To think this is really the 20th century. I must sit down a moment and collect myself. The *real* thing! [*He sits down.*]

ELLEN
You . . . you're not an American, are you?

KRETON
What a nice thought! No, I'm not.

JOHN
You sound more English.

KRETON
Do I? Is my accent very bad?

JOHN
No, it's quite good.

SPELDING
Where *are* you from, Mr. Kreton?

KRETON
[*Evasively.*] Another place.

SPELDING
On this earth of course.

KRETON
No, not on this planet.

ELLEN
Are you from Mars?

KRETON
Oh dear no, not Mars. There's nobody on Mars . . . at least no one I know.

ELLEN
I'm sure you're testing us and this is all some kind of publicity stunt.

KRETON
No, I really am from another place.

SPELDING
I don't suppose you'd consent to my interviewing you on television?

KRETON
I don't think your authorities will like that. They are terribly upset as it is.

SPELDING
How do you know?

KRETON
Well, I . . . pick up things. For instance, I know that in a few minutes a number of people from your Army will be here to question me and they . . . like you . . . are torn by doubt.

SPELDING
How extraordinary!

ELLEN
Why did you come here?

KRETON
Simply a visit to your small planet. I've been studying it for years. In fact, one might say, you people are my hobby. Especially, this period of your development.

JOHN
Are you the first person from your . . . your planet to travel in space like this?

KRETON
Oh my no! Everyone travels who wants to. It's just that no one wants to visit you. I can't think why. *I* always have. You'd be surprised what a thorough study I've made. [*Recites.*] The planet, Earth, is divided into five continents with a number of large islands. It is mostly water. There is one moon. Civilization is only just beginning. . . .

SPELDING
Just beginning! My dear sir, we have had. . . .

KRETON
[*Blandly.*] You are only in the initial stages, the most fascinating stage as far as I'm concerned . . . I do hope I don't sound patronizing.

ELLEN
Well, we are very proud.

KRETON
I know and that's one of your most endearing, primitive traits. Oh, I can't believe I'm here at last!

[GENERAL POWERS, *a vigorous product of the National Guard, and his* AIDE *enter.*]

POWERS

All right folks. The place is surrounded by troops. Where is the monster?

KRETON

I, my dear General, am the monster.

POWERS

What are you dressed up for, a fancy-dress party?

KRETON

I'd hoped to be in the costume of the period. As you see I am about a hundred years too late.

POWERS

Roger, who is this joker?

SPELDING

This is Mr. Kreton . . . General Powers. Mr. Kreton arrived in that thing outside. He is from another planet.

POWERS

I don't believe it.

ELLEN

It's true. We saw him get out of the flying saucer.

POWERS

[*To* AIDE.] Captain, go down and look at that ship. But be careful. Don't touch anything. And don't let anybody else near it. [AIDE *goes.*] So you're from another planet.

KRETON

Yes. My, that's a very smart uniform but I prefer the ones made of metal, the ones you used to wear, you know: with the feathers on top.

POWERS

That was five hundred years ago . . . Are you *sure* you're not from the Earth?

KRETON
Yes.

POWERS
Well, I'm not. You've got some pretty tall explaining to do.

KRETON
Anything to oblige.

POWERS
All right, which planet?

KRETON
None that you have ever heard of.

POWERS
Where is it?

KRETON
You wouldn't know.

POWERS
This solar system?

KRETON
No.

POWERS
Another system?

KRETON
Yes.

POWERS
Look, Buster, I don't want to play games: I just want to know where you're from. The law requires it.

KRETON
It's possible that I could explain it to a mathematician but I'm afraid I couldn't explain it to you, not for another five hundred years and by then of course *you'd* be dead because you people do die, don't you?

POWERS
What?

KRETON
Poor fragile butterflies, such brief little moments in the sun. . . . You see *we* don't die.

POWERS
You'll die all right if it turns out you're a spy or a hostile alien.

KRETON
I'm sure you wouldn't be so cruel.

[AIDE *returns; he looks disturbed.*]

POWERS
What did you find?

AIDE
I'm not sure, General.

POWERS
[*Heavily.*] Then do your best to describe what the object is like.

AIDE
Well, it's elliptical, with a fourteen-foot diameter. And it's made of an unknown metal which shines and inside there isn't anything.

POWERS
Isn't anything?

AIDE
There's nothing inside the ship: No instruments, no food, nothing.

POWERS
[*To* KRETON.] What did you do with your instrument board?

KRETON
With my what? Oh, I don't have one.

POWERS
How does the thing travel?

KRETON
I don't know.

POWERS
You don't know. Now look, Mister, you're in pretty serious trouble. I suggest you do a bit of cooperating. You claim you traveled here from outer space in a machine with no instruments . . .

KRETON
Well, these cars are rather common in my world and I suppose, once upon a time, I must've known the theory on which they operate but I've long since forgotten. After all, General, we're not mechanics, you and I.

POWERS
Roger, do you mind if we use your study?

SPELDING
Not at all. Not at all, General.

POWERS
Mr. Kreton and I are going to have a chat. [*To* AIDE.] Put in a call to the Chief of Staff.

AIDE
Yes, General.

[SPELDING *rises, leads* KRETON *and* POWERS *into next room, a handsomely furnished study, many books and a globe of the world.*]

SPELDING
This way, gentlemen.

[KRETON *sits down comfortably beside the globe which he twirls thoughtfully. At the door,* SPELDING *speaks in a low voice to* POWERS.]

I hope I'll be the one to get the story first, Tom.

POWERS
There isn't any story. Complete censorship. I'm sorry but this house is under martial law. I've a hunch we're in trouble.

[*He shuts the door.* SPELDING *turns and rejoins his family.*]

ELLEN
I think he's wonderful, whoever he is.

MRS. SPELDING
I wonder how much damage he did to my rose garden . . .

JOHN
It's sure hard to believe he's really from outer space. No instruments, no nothing . . . boy, they must be advanced scientifically.

MRS. SPELDING
Is he spending the night, dear?

SPELDING
What?

MRS. SPELDING
Is he spending the night?

SPELDING
Oh yes, yes, I suppose he will be.

MRS. SPELDING
Then I'd better go make up the bedroom. He seems perfectly nice to me. I like his whiskers. They're so very . . . comforting. Like Grandfather Spelding's. [*She goes.*]

SPELDING
[*Bitterly.*] I *know* this story will leak out before I can interview him. I just know it.

ELLEN
What does it mean, we're under martial law?

SPELDING
It means we have to do what General Powers tells us to do. [*He goes to the window as a soldier passes by.*] See?

JOHN
I wish I'd taken a closer look at that ship when I had the chance.

ELLEN
Perhaps he'll give us a ride in it.

JOHN
Traveling in space! Just like those stories. You know: intergalactic drive stuff.

SPELDING
If he's not an imposter.

ELLEN
I have a feeling he isn't.

JOHN
Well, I better call the family and tell them I'm all right.

[*He crosses to telephone by the door which leads into hall.*]

AIDE
I'm sorry, sir, but you can't use the phone.

SPELDING
He certainly can. This is my house . . .

AIDE
[*Mechanically.*] This house is a military reservation until the crisis is over: Order General Powers. I'm sorry.

JOHN
How am I to call home to say where I am?

AIDE
Only General Powers can help you. You're also forbidden to leave this house without permission.

SPELDING
You can't do this!

AIDE
I'm afraid, sir, we've done it.

ELLEN
Isn't it exciting!

[*Cut to study.*]

POWERS
Are you deliberately trying to confuse me?

KRETON
Not deliberately, no.

POWERS
We have gone over and over this for two hours now and all that you've told me is that you're from another planet in another solar system . . .

KRETON
In another dimension. I think that's the word you use.

POWERS
In another dimension and you have come here as a tourist.

KRETON
Up to a point, yes. What did you expect?

POWERS

It is my job to guard the security of this country.

KRETON

I'm sure that must be very interesting work.

POWERS

For all I know, you are a spy, sent here by an alien race to study us, preparatory to invasion.

KRETON

Oh, none of my people would *dream* of invading you.

POWERS

How do I know that's true?

KRETON

You don't, so I suggest you believe me. I should also warn you: I can tell what's inside.

POWERS

What's inside?

KRETON

What's inside your mind.

POWERS

You're a mind reader?

KRETON

I don't really read it. I hear it.

POWERS

What am I thinking?

KRETON

That I am either a lunatic from the earth or a spy from another world.

POWERS

Correct. But then you could've guessed that. [*Frowns.*] What am I thinking now?

KRETON

You're making a picture. Three silver stars. You're pinning them on your shoulder, instead of the two stars you now wear.

POWERS

[*Startled.*] That's right. I was thinking of my promotion.

KRETON

If there's anything I can do to hurry it along, just let me know.

POWERS

You can. Tell me why you're here.

KRETON

Well, we don't travel much, my people. We used to but since we see everything through special monitors and re-creators, there is no particular need to travel. However, *I* am a hobbyist. I love to gad about.

POWERS

[*Taking notes.*] Are you the first to visit us?

KRETON

Oh, no! We started visiting you long before there were people on the planet. However, we are seldom noticed on our trips. I'm sorry to say I slipped up, coming in the way I did . . . but then this visit was all rather impromptu. [*Laughs.*] I am a creature of impulse, I fear.

[AIDE *looks in.*]

AIDE

Chief of Staff on the telephone, General.

POWERS

[*Picks up phone.*] Hello, yes, sir. Powers speaking. I'm talking to him now. No, sir. No, sir. No, we can't determine what method of power was used. He won't talk. Yes, sir.

I'll hold him there. I've put the house under martial law
. . . belongs to a friend of mine, Roger Spelding, the TV
commentator. Roger Spelding, the TV . . . What? Oh,
no, I'm sure he won't say anything. Who . . . oh, yes, sir.
Yes, I realize the importance of it. Yes, I will. Good-by.
[*Hangs up.*] The President of the United States wants to
know all about you.

KRETON

How nice of him! And I want to know all about him. But
I do wish you'd let me rest a bit first. Your language is still
not familiar to me. I had to learn them all, quite exhaust-
ing.

POWERS

You speak *all* our languages?

KRETON

Yes, all of them. But then it's easier than you might think
since I can see what's inside.

POWERS

Speaking of what's inside, we're going to take your ship
apart.

KRETON

Oh, I wish you wouldn't.

POWERS

Security demands it.

KRETON

In that case *my* security demands you leave it alone.

POWERS

You plan to stop us?

KRETON

I already have . . . Listen.

[*Far-off shouting.* AIDE *rushes into the study.*]

AIDE

Something's happened to the ship, General. The door's
shut and there's some kind of wall all around it, an invisible wall. We can't get near it.

KRETON

[*To camera.*] I hope there was no one inside.

POWERS

[*To* KRETON.] How did you do that?

KRETON

I couldn't begin to explain. Now if you don't mind, I think
we should go in and see our hosts.

[*He rises, goes into living room.* POWERS *and* AIDE *look
at each other.*]

POWERS

Don't let him out of your sight.

[*Cut to living room as* POWERS *picks up phone.* KRETON
is with JOHN *and* ELLEN.]

KRETON

I don't mind curiosity but I really can't permit them to
wreck my poor ship.

ELLEN

What do you plan to do, now you're here?

KRETON

Oh, keep busy. I have a project or two . . . [*Sighs.*] I
can't believe you're real!

JOHN

Then we're all in the same boat.

KRETON

Boat? Oh, yes! Well, I should have come ages ago but
I . . . I couldn't get away until yesterday.

JOHN
Yesterday? It only took you a *day* to get here?

KRETON
One of *my* days, not yours. But then you don't know about time yet.

JOHN
Oh, you mean relativity.

KRETON
No, it's much more involved than that. You won't know about time until . . . now let me see if I remember . . . no, I don't, but it's about two thousand years.

JOHN
What do we do between now and then?

KRETON
You simply go on the way you are, living your exciting primitive lives . . . you have no idea how much fun you're having now.

ELLEN
I hope you'll stay with us while you're here.

KRETON
That's very nice of you. Perhaps I will. Though I'm sure you'll get tired of having a visitor underfoot all the time.

ELLEN
Certainly not. And Daddy will be deliriously happy. He can interview you by the hour.

JOHN
What's it like in outer space?

KRETON
Dull.

ELLEN
I should think it would be divine!

[POWERS *enters*.]

KRETON
No, General, it won't work.

POWERS
What won't work?

KRETON
Trying to blow up my little force field. You'll just plough up Mrs. Spelding's garden.

[POWERS *snarls and goes into study*.]

ELLEN
Can you tell what we're *all* thinking?

KRETON
Yes. As a matter of fact, it makes me a bit giddy. Your minds are not at all like ours. You see we control our thoughts while you . . . well, it's extraordinary the things you think about!

ELLEN
Oh, how awful! You can tell *everything* we think?

KRETON
Everything! It's one of the reasons I'm here, to intoxicate myself with your primitive minds . . . with the wonderful rawness of your emotions! You have no idea how it excites me! You simply seethe with unlikely emotions.

ELLEN
I've never felt so sordid.

JOHN
From now on I'm going to think about agriculture.

SPELDING
[*Entering.*] You would.

ELLEN
Daddy!

KRETON
No, no. You must go right on thinking about Ellen. Such wonderfully *purple* thoughts!

SPELDING
Now see here, Powers, you're carrying this martial law thing too far . . .

POWERS
Unfortunately, until I have received word from Washington as to the final disposition of this problem, you must obey my orders: no telephone calls, no communication with the outside.

SPELDING
This is unsupportable.

KRETON
Poor Mr. Spelding! If you like, I shall go. That would solve everything, wouldn't it?

POWERS
You're not going anywhere, Mr. Kreton, until I've had my instructions.

KRETON
I sincerely doubt if you could stop me. However, I put it up to Mr. Spelding. Shall I go?

SPELDING
Yes! [POWERS *gestures a warning.*] Do stay, I mean, we want you to get a good impression of us . . .

KRETON

And of course you still want to be the first journalist to interview me. Fair enough. All right, I'll stay on for a while.

POWERS

Thank you.

KRETON

Don't mention it.

SPELDING

General, may I ask our guest a few questions?

POWERS

Go right ahead, Roger. I hope you'll do better than I did.

SPELDING

Since you read our minds, you probably already know what our fears are.

KRETON

I do, yes.

SPELDING

We are afraid that you represent a hostile race.

KRETON

And I have assured General Powers that my people are not remotely hostile. Except for me, no one is interested in this planet's present stage.

SPELDING

Does this mean you might be interested in a *later* stage?

KRETON

I'm not permitted to discuss your future. Of course my friends think me perverse to be interested in a primitive society but there's no accounting for tastes, is there? You are my hobby. I love you. And that's all there is to it.

POWERS

So you're just here to look around . . . sort of going native.

KRETON

What a nice expression! That's it exactly. I am going native.

POWERS

[*Grimly.*] Well, it is my view that you have been sent here by another civilization for the express purpose of reconnoitering prior to invasion.

KRETON

That *would* be your view! The wonderfully primitive assumption that all strangers are hostile. You're almost too good to be true, General.

POWERS

You deny your people intend to make trouble for us?

KRETON

I deny it.

POWERS

Then are they interested in establishing communication with us? Trade? That kind of thing?

KRETON

We have always had communication with you. As for trade, well, we do not trade . . . that is something peculiar only to your social level. [*Quickly.*] Which I'm not criticizing! As you know, I approve of everything you do.

POWERS

I give up.

SPELDING

You have no interest then in . . . well, trying to dominate the earth.

KRETON
Oh, yes!

POWERS
I thought you just said your people weren't interested in us.

KRETON
They're not, but *I* am.

POWERS
You!

KRETON
Me . . . I mean I. You see I've come here to take charge.

POWERS
Of the United States?

KRETON
No, of the whole world. I'm sure you'll be much happier and it will be great fun for me. You'll get used to it in no time.

POWERS
This is ridiculous. How can one man take over the world?

KRETON
[*Gaily.*] Wait and see!

POWERS
[*To* AIDE.] Grab him!

[POWERS *and* AIDE *rush* KRETON *but within a foot of him, they stop, stunned.*]

KRETON
You can't touch me. That's part of the game. [*He yawns.*] Now, if you don't mind, I shall go up to my room for a little lie-down.

SPELDING

I'll show you the way.

KRETON

That's all right, I know the way. [*Touches his brow.*] Such savage thoughts! My head is vibrating like a drum. I feel quite giddy, all of you thinking away. [*He starts to the door; he pauses beside* MRS. SPELDING.] No, it's not a dream, dear lady. I shall be here in the morning when you wake up. And now, good night, dear, wicked children. . . .

[*He goes as we fade out.*]

ACT TWO

Fade in on KRETON'S *bedroom next morning. He lies fully clothed on bed with cat on his lap.*

KRETON

Poor cat! Of course I sympathize with you. Dogs *are* distasteful. What? Oh, I can well believe they do: yes, yes, how disgusting. They don't ever groom their fur! But you do *constantly*, such a fine coat. No, no, I'm not just saying that. I really mean it: exquisite texture. Of course, I wouldn't say it was *nicer* than skin but even so. . . . What? Oh, no! They *chase* you! Dogs chase you for no reason at all except pure malice? You poor creature. Ah, but you *do* fight back! That's right! Give it to them: slash, bite, scratch! Don't let them get away with a trick. . . . No! Do dogs really do that? Well, I'm sure *you* don't. What . . . oh, well, yes I completely agree about mice. They *are* delicious! (Ugh!) Pounce, snap and there is a heavenly dinner. No, I don't know any mice yet . . . they're not very amusing? But after all think how you must terrify them because you are so bold, so cunning, so beautifully predatory!

[*Knock at door.*]

Come in.

ELLEN

[*Enters.*] Good morning. I brought you your breakfast.

KRETON

How thoughtful! [*Examines bacon.*] Delicious, but I'm afraid my stomach is not like yours, if you'll pardon me. I don't eat. [*Removes pill from his pocket and swallows it.*] This is all I need for the day. [*Indicates cat.*] Unlike this creature, who would eat her own weight every hour, given a chance.

ELLEN

How do you know?

KRETON

We've had a talk.

ELLEN

You can *speak* to the cat?

KRETON

Not speak exactly but we communicate. I look inside and the cat cooperates. Bright red thoughts, very exciting, though rather on one level.

ELLEN

Does kitty like us?

KRETON

No, I wouldn't say she did. But then she has very few thoughts not connected with food. Have you, my quadruped criminal? [*He strokes the cat, which jumps to the floor.*]

ELLEN
You know you've really upset everyone.

KRETON
I supposed that I would.

ELLEN
Can you really take over the world, just like that?

KRETON
Oh, yes.

ELLEN
What do you plan to do when you *have* taken over?

KRETON
Ah, that is my secret.

ELLEN
Well, I think you'll be a very nice President, *if* they let you of course.

KRETON
What a sweet girl you are! Marry him right away.

ELLEN
Mary John?

KRETON
Yes. I see it in your head *and* in his. He wants you very much.

ELLEN
Well, we plan to get married this summer, if father doesn't fuss too much.

KRETON
Do it before then. I shall arrange it all if you like.

ELLEN
How?

KRETON

I can convince your father.

ELLEN

That sounds awfully ominous. I think you'd better leave poor Daddy alone.

KRETON

Whatever you say. [*Sighs.*] Oh, I love it so! When I woke up this morning I had to pinch myself to prove I was really here.

ELLEN

We were all doing a bit of pinching too. Ever since dawn we've had nothing but visitors and phone calls and troops outside in the garden. No one has the faintest idea what to do about you.

KRETON

Well, I don't think they'll be confused much longer.

ELLEN

How do you plan to conquer the world?

KRETON

I confess I'm not sure. I suppose I must make some demonstration of strength, some colorful trick that will frighten everyone . . . though I much prefer taking charge quietly. That's why I've sent for the President.

ELLEN

The President? *Our* President?

KRETON

Yes, he'll be along any minute now.

ELLEN

But the President just doesn't go around visiting people.

KRETON

He'll visit me. [*Chuckles.*] It may come as a surprise to him, but he'll be in this house in a very few minutes. I think we'd better go downstairs now. [*To cat.*] No, I will not give you a mouse. You must get your own. Be self-reliant. Beast!

[*Dissolve to the study.* POWERS *is reading book entitled: "The Atom and You." Muffled explosions off stage.*]

AIDE

[*Entering.*] Sir, nothing seems to be working. Do we have the General's permission to try a fission bomb on the force field?

POWERS

No . . . no. We'd better give it up.

AIDE

The men are beginning to talk.

POWERS

[*Thundering.*] Well, keep them quiet! [*Contritely.*] I'm sorry, Captain. I'm on edge. Fortunately, the whole business will soon be in the hands of the World Council.

AIDE

What will the World Council do?

POWERS

It will be interesting to observe them.

AIDE

You don't think this Kreton can really take over the world, do you?

POWERS

Of course not. Nobody can.

[*Dissolve to living room,* MRS. SPELDING *and* SPELDING *are talking.*]

MRS. SPELDING

You still haven't asked Mr. Kreton about moving that
thing, have you?

SPELDING

There are too many *important* things to ask him.

MRS. SPELDING

I hate to be a nag but you know the trouble I have had
getting anything to grow in that part of the garden . . .

JOHN

[*Enters.*] Good morning.

MRS. SPELDING

Good morning, John.

JOHN

Any sign of your guest?

MRS. SPELDING

Ellen took his breakfast up to him a few minutes ago.

JOHN

They don't seem to be having much luck, do they? I sure
hope you don't mind my staying here like this.

[SPELDING *glowers.*]

MRS. SPELDING

Why, we love having you! I just hope your family aren't
too anxious.

JOHN

One of the G.I.'s finally called them, said I was staying
here for the weekend.

SPELDING

The rest of our *lives,* if something isn't done soon.

JOHN
Just how long do you think that'll be, Dad?

SPELDING
Who knows?

[KRETON *and* ELLEN *enter.*]

KRETON
Ah, how wonderful to see you again! Let me catch my breath. . . . Oh, your minds! It's not easy for me, you know. So many crude thoughts blazing away! Yes, Mrs. Spelding, I will move the ship off your roses.

MRS. SPELDING
That's awfully sweet of you.

KRETON
Mr. Spelding, if any interviews are to be granted you will be the first. I promise you.

SPELDING
That's very considerate, I'm sure.

KRETON
So you can stop thinking *those* particular thoughts. And now where is the President?

SPELDING
The President?

KRETON
Yes, I sent for him. He should be here. [*He goes to the terrace window.*] Ah, that must be he.

[*A swarthy man in uniform with a sash across his chest is standing, bewildered, on the terrace.* KRETON *opens the glass doors.*]

Come in, sir, come in, Your Excellency. Good of you to come on such short notice.

[MAN *enters.*]

MAN
[*In Spanish accent.*] Where am I?

KRETON
You *are* the President, aren't you?

MAN
Of course I am the President. What am I doing here? I
was dedicating a bridge and I find myself . . .

KRETON
[*Aware of his mistake.*] Oh, dear! *Where* was the bridge?

MAN
Where do you think, you idiot, in Paraguay!

KRETON
[*To others.*] I seem to've made a mistake. Wrong President.
[*Gestures and the* MAN *disappears.*] Seemed rather upset,
didn't he?

JOHN
You can make people come and go just like that?

KRETON
Just like that.

[POWERS *looks into room from the study.*]

POWERS
Good morning, Mr. Kreton. Could I see you for a moment?

KRETON
By all means. [*He crosses to the study.*]

SPELDING
I believe I am going mad.

[*Cut to study. The* AIDE *stands at attention while*

POWERS *addresses* KRETON.]

POWERS
. . . and so we feel, the government of the United States feels, that this problem is too big for any one country, therefore we are turning the whole affair over to Paul Laurent, the Secretary-General of the World Council.

KRETON
Very sensible. I should've thought of that myself.

POWERS
Mr. Laurent is on his way here now. And I may add, Mr. Kreton, you've made me look singularly ridiculous.

KRETON
I'm awfully sorry. [*Pause.*] No, you can't kill me.

POWERS
You were reading my mind again.

KRETON
I can't really help it, you know. And such *black* thoughts today, but intense, very intense.

POWERS
I regard you as a menace.

KRETON
I know you do and I think it's awfully unkind. I do mean well.

POWERS
Then go back where you came from and leave us alone.

KRETON
I'm afraid I can't do that just yet . . .

[*Phone rings, the* AIDE *answers it.*]

AIDE

He's outside? Sure, let him through. [*To* POWERS.] The Secretary-General of the World Council is here sir.

POWERS

[*To* KRETON.] I hope you'll listen to *him*.

KRETON

Oh, I shall, of course. I love listening.

[*The door opens and* PAUL LAURENT, *middle-aged and serene, enters.* POWERS *and his* AIDE *stand to attention.* KRETON *goes forward to shake hands.*]

LAURENT

Mr. Kreton?

KRETON

At your service, Mr. Laurent.

LAURENT

I welcome you to this planet in the name of the World Council.

KRETON

Thank you sir, thank you.

LAURENT

Could you leave us alone for a moment, General?

POWERS

Yes, sir.

[POWERS *and* AIDE *go.* LAURENT *smiles at* KRETON.]

LAURENT

Shall we sit down?

KRETON

Yes, yes I love sitting down. I'm afraid my manners are not quite suitable, yet.

[*They sit down.*]

LAURENT
Now, Mr. Kreton, in violation of all the rules of diplomacy, may I come to the point? ·

KRETON
You may.

LAURENT
Why are you here?

KRETON
Curiosity. Pleasure.

LAURENT
You are a tourist then in this time and place?

KRETON
[*Nods.*] Yes. Very well put.

LAURENT
We have been informed that you have extraordinary powers.

KRETON
By your standards, yes, they must seem extraordinary.

LAURENT
We have also been informed that it is your intention to . . . to take charge of this world.

KRETON
That is correct. . . . What a remarkable mind you have! I have difficulty looking inside it.

LAURENT
[*Laughs.*] Practice. I've attended so many conferences. . . . May I say that your conquest of our world puts your status of tourist in a rather curious light?

KRETON
Oh, I said nothing about *conquest.*

LAURENT
Then how else do you intend to govern? The people won't
allow you to direct their lives without a struggle.

KRETON
But I'm sure they will if I ask them to.

LAURENT
You believe you can do all this without, well, without
violence?

KRETON
Of course I can. One or two demonstrations and I'm sure
they'll do as I ask. [*Smiles.*] Watch this.

[*Pause: Then shouting.* POWERS *bursts into room.*]

POWERS
Now what've you done?

KRETON
Look out the window, your Excellency.

[LAURENT *goes to window. A rifle floats by, followed by
an alarmed soldier.*]

Nice, isn't it? I confess I worked out a number of rather
melodramatic tricks last night. Incidentally, all the rifles
of all the soldiers in all the world are now floating in the
air. [*Gestures.*] Now they have them back.

POWERS
[*To* LAURENT.] You see, sir, I didn't exaggerate in my report.

LAURENT
[*Awed.*] No, no, you certainly didn't.

KRETON

You were skeptical, weren't you?

LAURENT

Naturally. But now I . . . now I think it's possible.

POWERS

That this . . . this gentleman is going to run everything?

LAURENT

Yes, yes I do. And it might be wonderful.

KRETON

You *are* more clever than the others. You begin to see that I mean only good.

LAURENT

Yes, only good. General, do you realize what this means? We can have one government . . .

KRETON

With innumerable bureaus, and intrigue. . . .

LAURENT

[*Excited.*] And the world could be incredibly prosperous, especially if he'd help us with his superior knowledge.

KRETON

[*Delighted.*] I will, I will. I'll teach you to look into one another's minds. You'll find it devastating but enlightening: all that self-interest, those *lurid* emotions . . .

LAURENT

No more countries. No more wars . . .

KRETON

[*Startled.*] What? Oh, but I like a lot of countries. Besides, at this stage of your development you're supposed to have lots of countries and lots of wars . . . innumerable wars . . .

LAURENT
But you can help us change all that.

KRETON
Change all that! My dear sir, I am your friend.

LAURENT
What do you mean?

KRETON
Why, your deepest pleasure is violence. How can you deny that? It is the whole point to you, the whole point to my hobby . . . and you are my hobby, all mine.

LAURENT
But our lives are devoted to *controlling* violence, and not creating it.

KRETON
Now, don't take me for an utter fool. After all, I can see into your minds. My dear fellow, don't you *know* what you are?

LAURENT
What are we?

KRETON
You are savages. I have returned to the dark ages of an insignificant planet simply because I want the glorious excitement of being among you and reveling in your savagery! There is murder in all your hearts and I love it! It intoxicates me!

LAURENT
[*Slowly.*] You hardly flatter us.

KRETON
I didn't mean to be rude but you did ask me why I am here and I've told you.

LAURENT

You have no wish then to . . . to help us poor savages.

KRETON

I couldn't even if I wanted to. You won't be civilized for at least two thousand years and you won't reach the level of my people for about a million years.

LAURENT

[*Sadly.*] Then you have come here only to . . . to observe?

KRETON

No, more than that. I mean to regulate your past times. But don't worry: I won't upset things too much. I've decided I don't want to be known to the people. You will go right on with your countries, your squabbles, the way you always have, while I will *secretly* regulate things through you.

LAURENT

The World Council does not govern. We only advise.

KRETON

Well, I shall advise you and you will advise the governments and we shall have a lovely time.

LAURENT

I don't know what to say. You obviously have the power to do as you please.

KRETON

I'm glad you realize that. Poor General Powers is now wondering if a hydrogen bomb might destroy me. It won't, General.

POWERS

Too bad.

KRETON

Now, your Excellency, I shall stay in this house until you have laid the groundwork for my first project.

LAURENT

And what is that to be?

KRETON

A war! I want one of your really splendid wars, with all the trimmings, all the noise and the fire . . .

LAURENT

A war! You're joking. Why at this moment we are working as hard as we know how *not* to have a war.

KRETON

But secretly you want one. After all, it's the one thing your little race does well. You'd hardly want me to deprive you of your simple pleasures, now would you?

LAURENT

I think you must be mad.

KRETON

Not mad, simply a philanthropist. Of course I myself shall get a great deal of pleasure out of a war (the vibrations must be incredible!) but I'm doing it mostly for you. So, if you don't mind, I want you to arrange a few incidents, so we can get one started spontaneously.

LAURENT

I refuse.

KRETON

In that event, I shall select someone else to head the World Council. Someone who *will* start a war. I suppose there exist a few people here who might like the idea.

LAURENT

How can you do such a horrible thing to us? Can't you see

that we don't want to be savages?

KRETON
But you have no choice. Anyway, you're just pulling my
leg! I'm sure you want a war as much as the rest of them
do and that's what you're going to get: the biggest war
you've ever had!

LAURENT
[*Stunned.*] Heaven help us!

KRETON
[*Exuberant.*] Heaven won't! Oh, what fun it will be! I can
hardly wait! [*He strikes the globe of the world a happy
blow as we fade out.*]

ACT THREE

Fade in on the study, two weeks later. KRETON *is sitting at
desk on which a map is spread out. He has a pair of divid-
ers, some models of jet aircraft. Occassionally he pretends
to dive-bomb, imitating the sound of a bomb going off.*
POWERS *enters.*

POWERS
You wanted me, sir?

KRETON
Yes, I wanted those figures on radioactive fallout.

POWERS
They're being made up now, sir. Anything else?

KRETON
Oh, my dear fellow, why do you dislike me so?

POWERS

I am your military aide, sir: I don't have to answer that question. It is outside the sphere of my duties.

KRETON

Aren't you at least happy about your promotion?

POWERS

Under the circumstances, no, sir.

KRETON

I find your attitude baffling.

POWERS

Is that all, sir?

KRETON

You have never once said what you thought of my war plans. Not once have I got a single word of encouragement from you, a single compliment . . . only black thoughts.

POWERS

Since you read my mind, sir, you know what I think.

KRETON

True, but I can't help but feel that deep down inside of you there is just a twinge of professional jealousy. You don't like the idea of an outsider playing your game better than you do. Now confess!

POWERS

I am acting as your aide only under duress.

KRETON

[*Sadly.*] Bitter, bitter . . . and to think I chose you especially as my aide. Think of all the other generals who would give anything to have your job.

POWERS

Fortunately, they know nothing about my job.

KRETON

Yes, I do think it wise not to advertise my presence, don't you?

POWERS

I can't see that it makes much difference, since you seem bent on destroying our world.

KRETON

I'm not going to destroy it. A few dozen cities, that's all, and not very nice cities either. Think of the fun you'll have building new ones when it's over.

POWERS

How many millions of people do you plan to kill?

KRETON

Well, quite a few, but they love this sort of thing. You can't convince me they don't. Oh, I know what Laurent says. But he's a misfit, out of step with this time. Fortunately, my new World Council is more reasonable.

POWERS

Paralyzed is the word, sir.

KRETON

You don't think they like me either?

POWERS

You *know* they hate you, sir.

KRETON

But love and hate are so confused in your savage minds and the vibrations of the one are so very like those of the other that I can't always distinguish. You see, we neither love nor hate in my world. We simply have hobbies. [*He strokes the globe of the world tenderly.*] But now to work. Tonight's the big night: first, the sneak attack, then: boom! [*He claps his hands gleefully.*]

[*Dissolve to the living room, to* JOHN *and* ELLEN.]

ELLEN
I've never felt so helpless in my life.

JOHN
Here we all stand around doing nothing while he plans to blow up the world.

ELLEN
Suppose we went to the newspapers.

JOHN
He controls the press. When Laurent resigned they didn't even print his speech.

[*A gloomy pause.*]

ELLEN
What are you thinking about, John?

JOHN
Walnuts.

[*They embrace.*]

ELLEN
Can't we do anything?

JOHN
No, I guess there's nothing.

ELLEN
[*Vehemently.*] Oh! I could kill him!

[KRETON *and* POWERS *enter.*]

KRETON
Very good, Ellen, *very* good! I've never felt you so violent.

ELLEN
You heard what I said to John?

KRETON

Not in words, but you were absolutely bathed in malevolence.

POWERS

I'll get the papers you wanted, sir. [POWERS *exits*.]

KRETON

I don't think he likes me very much but your father does. Only this morning he offered to handle my public relations and I said I'd let him. Wasn't that nice of him?

JOHN

I think I'll go get some fresh air. [*He goes out through the terrace door.*]

KRETON

Oh, dear! [*Sighs.*] Only your father is really entering the spirit of the game. He's a much better sport than you, my dear.

ELLEN

[*Exploding.*] Sport! That's it! You think we're sport. You think we're animals to be played with: well, we're not. We're people and we don't want to be destroyed.

KRETON

[*Patiently.*] But *I* am not destroying you. You will be destroying one another of your own free will, as you have always done. I am simply a . . . a kibitzer.

ELLEN

No, you are a vampire!

KRETON

A vampire? You mean I drink blood? Ugh!

ELLEN

No, you drink emotions, our emotions. You'll sacrifice us all for the sake of your . . . your vibrations!

KRETON

Touché. Yet what harm am I really doing? It's true I'll enjoy the war more than anybody; but it will be *your* destructiveness after all, not mine.

ELLEN

You could stop it.

KRETON

So could you.

ELLEN

I?

KRETON

Your race. They could stop altogether but they won't. And I can hardly intervene in their natural development. The most I can do is help out in small, practical ways.

ELLEN

We are not what you think. We're not so . . . so primitive.

KRETON

My dear girl, just take this one household: your mother dislikes your father but she is too tired to do anything about it so she knits and she gardens and she tries not to think about him. Your father, on the other hand, is bored with all of you. Don't look shocked: he doesn't like you any more than you like him . . .

ELLEN

Don't say that!

KRETON

I am only telling you the truth. Your father wants you to marry someone important; therefore he objects to John while you, my girl . . .

ELLEN
[*With a fierce cry,* ELLEN *grabs vase to throw.*] You devil!
[*Vase breaks in her hand.*]

KRETON
You see? That proves my point perfectly. [*Gently.*] Poor
savage, I cannot help what you are. [*Briskly.*] Anyway, you
will soon be distracted from your personal problems. Tonight is the night. If you're a good girl, I'll let you watch
the bombing.

[*Dissolve to study: Eleven forty-five.* POWERS *and the*
AIDE *gloomily await the war.*]

AIDE
General, isn't there anything we can do?

POWERS
It's out of our hands.

[KRETON, *dressed as a Hussar with shako, enters.*]

KRETON
Everything on schedule?

POWERS
Yes, sir. Planes left for their targets at twenty-two hundred.

KRETON
Good . . . good. I myself, shall take off shortly after midnight to observe the attack first hand.

POWERS
Yes, sir.

[KRETON *goes into the living room where the family is
gloomily assembled.*]

KRETON
[*Enters from study.*] And now the magic hour approaches!

I hope you're all as thrilled as I am.

SPELDING
You still won't tell us who's attacking whom?

KRETON
You'll know in exactly . . . fourteen minutes.

ELLEN
[*Bitterly.*] Are we going to be killed too?

KRETON
Certainly not! You're quite safe, at least in the early stages of the war.

ELLEN
Thank you.

MRS. SPELDING
I suppose this will mean rationing again.

SPELDING
Will . . . will we see anything from here?

KRETON
No, but there should be a good picture on the monitor in the study. Powers is tuning in right now.

JOHN
[*At window.*] Hey look, up there! Coming this way!

[*Ellen joins him.*]

ELLEN
What is it?

JOHN
Why . . . it's *another* one! And it's going to land.

KRETON
[*Surprised.*] I'm sure you're mistaken. No one would dream of coming here. [*He has gone to the window, too.*]

ELLEN
It's landing!

SPELDING
Is it a friend of yours, Mr. Kreton?

KRETON
[*Slowly.*] No, no, not a friend . . . [KRETON *retreats to the study; he inadvertently drops a lace handerchief beside the sofa.*]

JOHN
Here he comes.

ELLEN
[*Suddenly bitter.*] Now we have two of them.

MRS. SPELDING
My poor roses.

[*The new* VISITOR *enters in a gleam of light from his ship. He is wearing a most futuristic costume. Without a word, he walks past the awed family into the study.* KRETON *is cowering behind the globe.* POWERS *and the* AIDE *stare, bewildered, as the* VISITOR *gestures sternly and* KRETON *reluctantly removes shako and sword. They communicate by odd sounds.*]

VISITOR
[*To* POWERS.] Please leave us alone.

[*Cut to living room as* POWERS *and the* AIDE *enter from the study.*]

POWERS
[*To* ELLEN.] Who on earth was that?

ELLEN
It's another one, another visitor.

POWERS
Now we're done for.

ELLEN
I'm going in there.

MRS. SPALDING
Ellen, don't you dare!

ELLEN
I'm going to talk to them. [*Starts to door.*]

JOHN
I'm coming, too.

ELLEN
[*Grimly.*] No, alone. I know what I want to say.

[*Cut to interior of the study, to* KRETON *and the other* VISITOR *as* ELLEN *enters.*]

ELLEN
I want you both to listen to me . . .

VISITOR
You don't need to speak. I know what you will say.

ELLEN
That you have no right here? That you mustn't . . .

VISITOR
I agree. Kreton has no right here. He is well aware that it is forbidden to interfere with the past.

ELLEN
The past?

VISITOR
[*Nods.*] You are the past, the dark ages: we are from the future. In fact, we are *your* descendants on another planet. We visit you from time to time but we never inter-

fere because it would change *us* if we did. Fortunately, I have arrived in time.

ELLEN
There won't be a war?

VISITOR
There will be no war. And there will be no memory of any of this. When we leave here you will forget Kreton and me. Time will turn back to the moment before his arrival.

ELLEN
Why did you want to hurt us?

KRETON
[*Heart-broken.*] Oh, but I didn't! I only wanted to have . . . well, to have a little fun, to indulge my hobby . . . against the rules of course.

VISITOR
[*To* ELLEN.] Kreton is a rarity among us. Mentally and morally he is retarded. He is a child and he regards your period as his toy.

KRETON
A child, now really!

VISITOR
He escaped from his nursery and came back in time to you . . .

KRETON
And *every*thing went wrong, everything! I wanted to visit 1860 . . . that's my *real* period but then something happened to the car and I ended up here, not that I don't find you nearly as interesting but . . .

VISITOR
We must go, Kreton.

KRETON
[*To* ELLEN.] You did like me just a bit, didn't you?

ELLEN
Yes, yes I did, until you let your hobby get out of hand.
[*To* VISITOR.] What is the future like?

VISITOR
Very serene, very different . . .

KRETON
Don't believe him: it is dull, dull, dull beyond belief! One
simply floats through eternity: no wars, no excitement . . .

VISITOR
It is forbidden to discuss these matters.

KRETON
I can't see what difference it makes since she's going to
forget all about us anyway.

ELLEN
Oh, how I'd love to see the future . . .

VISITOR
It is against . . .

KRETON
Against the rules: how tiresome, you are [*To* ELLEN.] But,
alas, you can never pay us a call because you aren't born
yet! I mean where we are you are not. Oh, Ellen, dear,
think kindly of me, until you forget.

ELLEN
I will.

VISITOR
Come. Time has begun to turn back. Time is bending.

[*He starts to door.* KRETON *turns conspiratorially to*
ELLEN.]

KRETON

Don't be sad, my girl. I shall be back one bright day, but a bright day in 1860. I dote on the Civil War, so exciting . . .

VISITOR

Kreton!

KRETON

Only next time I think it'll be more fun if the *South* wins! [*He hurries after the* VISITOR.]

[*Cut to clock as the hands spin backwards. Dissolve to the living room, exactly the same as the first scene:* SPELDING, MRS. SPELDING, ELLEN.]

SPELDING

There is nothing wrong with marrying a wealthy man. The horror of it has always eluded me. However, my only wish is that you marry someone hard-working, ambitious, a man who'll make his mark in the world. Not a boy who is content to sit on a farm all his life, growing peanuts . . .

ELLEN

English walnuts! And he won't just sit there.

SPELDING

Will you stop contradicting me?

ELLEN

But, Daddy, John grows walnuts . . .

[JOHN *enters.*]

JOHN

Hello, everybody.

MRS. SPELDING

Good evening, John.

ELLEN
What kept you, darling? You missed Daddy's broadcast.

JOHN
I saw it before I left home. Wonderful broadcast, sir.

SPELDING
Thank you, John.

[JOHN *crosses to window.*]

JOHN
That meteor you were talking about, well, for a while it looked almost like a space ship or something. You can just barely see it now.

[*Ellen joins him at window. They watch, arms about one another.*]

SPELDING
Space ship! Nonsense! Remarkable what some people will believe, *want* to believe. Besides, as I said in the broadcast: if there's any traveling to be done in space we'll do it first.

[*He notices* KRETON'S *handkerchief on sofa and picks it up. They all look at it, puzzled, as we cut to stock shot of the starry night against which two space ships vanish in the distance, one serene in its course, the other erratic, as we fade out.*]

BIOGRAPHICAL NOTES

WILLIAM SAROYAN: Before writing a full-length play, William Saroyan (1908-   ) had gained national recognition as a short-story writer. *The Daring Young Man on the Flying Trapeze* (1934) had launched his storywriting career, and his rapid writing pace had resulted in five collections of stories in the ensuing five years. *The Time of Your Life* (1939) was Saroyan's first full-length play, and for it he was offered the Pulitzer Prize and the New York Drama Critics' Award for the 1939-40 season. Never backward in estimating his own ability, Saroyan refused the Pulitzer Prize on the ground that the play was no better than anything else he had written. Although several other full-length plays have followed, Saroyan has not again attained the critical praise accorded *The Time of Your Life*. Two of his short plays, *My Heart's in the Highlands* (1939) and *Hello, Out There* (1942), are still extensively produced throughout the country. In 1955, *The Time of Your Life* was successfully revived at New York's City Center. Besides being a short-story writer and dramatist, Saroyan has written novels and collaborated with a cousin of his to produce the popular song hit of 1951, "Come on-a My House." *The Human Comedy* (1943) is typical and the most popular of his novels. At present, Saroyan writes scripts for *Candid Camera,* a television show. His best work is concerned with the goodness of man, and Saroyan's impressionistic style lends itself brilliantly to this optimistic theme.

TENNESSEE WILLIAMS: Tennessee Williams (1914-) received his first recognition as a dramatist from the Group Theater in 1939 for *American Blues,* four short plays. His full-length *Battle of Angels* was produced in 1940, but casting and Boston censorship quickly ended the play's pre-Broadway trial. Departing from realistic drama, Williams wrote *The Glass Menagerie* (1944), which won the New York Drama Critics' Award. His next big achievement was *A Streetcar Named Desire,* and it earned him the New York Drama Critics' Award and the Pulitzer Prize for the 1947-48 season. After several minor successes, Williams won these same two awards again, for *Cat on a Hot Tin Roof* (1955). *Battle of Angels* was revised and, as *Orpheus Descending* (1956), met with wide approval. Turning from the darker side of life, Williams gave 1960 audiences a comedy, *Period of Adjustment.* Recent plays include *The Night of the Iguana* and *The Milk Train Doesn't Stop Here Anymore.* Williams' best plays to date are concerned with the theme of decadence in the South; frustrated and faded, his heroines are symbols of this decadence. Williams' work is enriched by his gift for lyrical dialogue; experimenting with the stage and scenery in an effort to replace realism with symbolism, Williams has gotten beneath the surface of things to give the theater a new form of dramatic poetry.

THORNTON WILDER: Awarded the Pulitzer Prize for his novel, *The Bridge of San Luis Rey* (1927), Thornton

Wilder (1897-   ) then gave some of his attention to the writing of short plays and soon produced two collections of them. Extending his dramatic craft to include full-length presentations, Wilder was awarded the 1937-38 Pulitzer Prize for *Our Town*. Wilder's adaptation of the German play, *The Merchant of Yonkers,* failed on Broadway the next season, but he triumphantly returned to Broadway with *The Skin of Our Teeth* (1942), which brought him his third Pulitzer Prize. Retaining his interest in other literary endeavors, Wilder published a highly praised novel, *The Ides of March,* in 1948. The American Academy of Arts and Letters added to Wilder's impressive awards by granting him a Gold Medal for Fiction in 1952. Three years later Wilder gave Broadway another look at *The Merchant of Yonkers*. Revised and retitled *The Matchmaker,* it was favorably received. His recent short plays, *Plays for Bleeker Street* (1962), were written for off-Broadway production. Wilder is an original experimenter in imaginative presentation, as against realistic representation, for the American theater. *Our Town,* Wilder's most successful play, makes no attempt to create the illusion of reality characteristic of most modern drama. Devoid of a conventional stage setting, *Our Town* necessitates and restores audience imagination. In all his writings, Wilder examines the human experience and presents it with a simplicity that only a deep understanding can successfully sustain.

SUSAN GLASPELL: Having written several short stories and novels, Susan Glaspell (1882-1948) became interested in dramatic writing when her husband, George Cram Cook, organized the Provincetown Players in 1915. Her first attempt was the successful *Trifles,* a one-act play, written in 1916, and she collaborated with her husband to write *Suppressed Desires* the following year. Before the death of Cook in 1923, she had written several other short dramas and three full-length plays. Continuing to write both drama and fiction, Susan Glaspell received the 1931 Pulitzer Prize for the play, *Alison's House*. After winning this award, she stopped writing for the theater. During the remaining seventeen years of her life, she wrote four more novels. Susan Glaspell's early years were spent in the Middle West, and most of her writings depict the life in that area. In contrast, the heroine of her most successful work, the Pulitzer Prize-winning *Alison's House,* leads a life which closely resembles that of the New England poet, Emily Dickinson. Although sometimes criticized for a lack of real content, Susan Glaspell's works are generally acknowledged to have a strength deriving from her sensitive, sympathetic handling of characters.

SHERWOOD ANDERSON: At the age of thirty-six, Sherwood Anderson (1876-1941) left his paint factory in Elyria, Ohio, and went to Chicago. There he began to write, and for the next three years he contributed stories and essays to the well-known magazine, *The Little Review.* When Anderson published his famous tales of life in small-town Ohio, *Winesburg, Ohio* (1919), he already had two novels and a book of poems in print. By 1921, he had added *Poor White,* a novel, and *The Triumph of the Egg,* originally a book of tales and poems of American life. For the latter he received the *Dial* Award of two thousand dollars. During the following two decades, Sherwood Anderson wrote several novels, several books of short stories, poems, biographical sketches and essays, and four plays. One of the plays was a dramatization of *Winesburg, Ohio.* The style and theme of much of Anderson's writing can be seen in the interrelated stories of *Winesburg, Ohio;* his "grotesques," as he called the characters in these stories, supply vivid portraits of the human frustrations faced in small-town Midwestern life early in the century. Anderson frees these inhibited souls through a technique that substitutes symbolic acts for realistic acts. The strength of almost all of Anderson's fictional characters lies not in their life-likeness but rather in the strange, mysterious, almost supernatural impression which they leave upon the reader.

MAXWELL ANDERSON: After joining with Laurence Stallings to write the extremely realistic and highly praised drama of men in war, *What Price Glory* (1924), Maxwell Anderson (1888-1959) soon decided to write plays in verse. He felt that the use of poetic expression would elevate the modern theater. *Elizabeth the Queen* (1930) was the first of several plays which were successful in bringing historical figures to life. Three years later Anderson won the Pulitzer Prize for *Both Your Houses*. Determined to restore poetry as the language of the theater, he followed with *Mary of Scotland* (1933) and *Valley Forge* (1934). During the next two seasons, Anderson was the recipient of the New York Drama Critics' Award for *Winterset* (1935) and *High Tor* (1936). Although the plays that followed in the next two decades did not receive the critical praise of the two just mentioned, they were in most instances popular with theatergoers. Anderson's use of verse in a variety of dramatic situations for commercial theater was an experiment that succeeded. His *High Tor* was a fantasy, *Winterset* was a tragedy. The Sacco-Vanzetti case formed the framework for *Winterset*, but the play goes beyond its contemporary social problem and its setting to explore man's universal quest for justice. All of Anderson's tragedies, whether contemporary or historical in setting, probe universal problems. He is the only American playwright to have made anything like a consistent success of verse drama on Broadway.

PAUL GREEN: Born on his father's farm in North Carolina, Paul Green (1894-   ) spent his early years working with the Negro laborers employed by his father. At the University of North Carolina, Green began to use his knowledge of Negro life in the creation of short folk dramas. He soon extended his writing to include the full-length drama, and in 1927 two of his plays were produced on Broadway. One of them, *In Abraham's Bosom,* won the Pulitzer Prize for that season. The following year Green was granted a Guggenheim Fellowship for study abroad, and he spent the time writing and studying in Germany and England. In 1936 he collaborated with Kurt Weill to produce *Johnny Johnson* for the Group Theater, whose first production had been Green's *The House of Connelly* (1931). In 1937 he began to experiment with music, song, dance, and pantomime, working them together into large outdoor productions which he named "symphonic dramas." The first of these plays, *The Lost Colony,* was successfully produced in a large amphitheater in North Carolina. This play, in which 150 people took part, became a significant factor in the development of the American community theater. Continuing with plays for outdoor production, he wrote *The Highland Call* (1941) and then *The Common Glory* (1948); they are two "symphonic dramas of American history" that are being produced almost yearly. His most recent work is *The Stephen Foster Story* (1959). Green's plays, short or full-length, make use of rhythms and music; both his outdoor works and his conventional works have been highly successful. His prize-winning tragedy, *In Abraham's Bosom,* is much more than a dramatized folk tale of Negro life. The play goes beneath its particular social problem and into man's inner spiritual and emotional conflicts.

NORMAN CORWIN: Norman Corwin (1910-   ) had written for several newspapers in Boston before he left for New York City in 1936. From journalism he moved into the field of radio drama and was signed by the Columbia Broadcasting System in 1941 to do a series of plays titled *26 by Corwin.* They were well received, and an equally successful series *Columbia Presents Corwin,* followed. Corwin's efforts to increase human understanding were acknowledged, and, besides numerous other awards, he was given the 1944-45 Distinguished Merit Award of the National Conference of Christians and Jews. Continuing to write radio dramas, Corwin was judged the winner of the 1946 Wendell Willkie One World Flight Award. His ability to handle themes concerned with universal human relations prompted the United Nations to name him for a position of Chief of Special Projects in Radio for 1949. Four years later, Corwin published his first novel, *Dog in the Sky.* Corwin presently resides in California and has added motion picture and television scripts to his writing credits.

GORE VIDAL: Embarking on a writing career early in life, Gore Vidal (1925-   ) had his first novel, *Williwaw,* published when he was twenty-one years of age. He wrote the novel while a first mate on an Army freight-supply ship in the Aleutians. Three other novels followed, along with many television and film scripts. In 1956, his *Visit to a Small Planet* was presented on Broadway and instantly acclaimed. Later versions of the play were equally well received. Politics played an important role in Vidal's life during 1960. Running as a member of the Democratic Party in New York's Dutchess County, he made an unsuccessful bid for Congress, but his political comedy, *The Best Man,* made a successful bid for Broadway and was one of the hits of the season. He recently published *Rocking the Boat* (1962), a book of essays, and is presently working on the life of a fourth-century Roman Emperor, Julian the Apostate. Vidal is a versatile writer; his published works include even a mystery novel, *Death Before Bedtime,* written under the pseudonym of Edgar Box.